BRIGHT IDEAS

Inspirations for INVESTIGATIONS IN SCIENCE

Published by Scholastic
Publications Ltd,
Villiers House,
Clarendon Avenue,
Leamington Spa,
Warwickshire CV32 5PR

© 1993 Scholastic Publications Ltd

Written by Colin Hughes and
Winnie Wade
Edited by Ann Marangos
Sub-edited by Jane Wright
Designed by Sue Limb
Series designed by Juanita
Puddifoot
Illustrated by Ann Johns and Chris
Saunderson
Cover design by Micky Pledge
Cover artwork by Conny Jude

Designed using Aldus Pagemaker
Processed by Pages Bureau,
Leamington Spa
Artwork by David Harban Design,
Warwick
Printed in Great Britain by
Ebenezer Baylis & Son, Worcester

**British Library Cataloguing in
Publication Data**
A catalogue record for this book is
available from the British Library.

ISBN 0-590-53027-5

CONTENTS

INTRODUCTION

Science in the National Curriculum

Science in the National Curriculum (1991) sees the essential elements of a developing experience of science as being 'to communicate, to relate science to everyday life and to explore'. As children gain increased knowledge and understanding they should be given the opportunity to develop an awareness of the importance of science in everyday life. This awareness can be developed through investigation.

Children should, therefore, develop the intellectual and practical skills which will allow them to explore and investigate the world of science.

The investigative skills fundamental to science as an investigative, enquiry-based discipline include:
• observing and interpreting observations;
• assessing similarities and differences;
• finding patterns and making predictions;
• identifying problems and raising questions;
• hypothesising;
• planning and carrying out investigations by experiment;
• fair testing and testing of hypotheses;
• collecting, recording and communicating findings in a number of appropriate forms;
• drawing inferences based on the findings obtained;
• evaluating the validity of findings.

BACKGROUND

These skills are grouped together in the following way in *Science in the National Curriculum* (1991) under:

Attainment target 1: Scientific investigation
(i) ask questions, predict and hypothesise;
(ii) observe, measure and manipulate variables;
(iii) interpret results and evaluate scientific evidence.

The knowledge and understanding to be covered within the Science National Curriculum is now set out under three attainment targets:

Attainment target 2: Life and living processes
This attainment target includes understanding of life processes, variation in populations, and a study of ecosystems.

Attainment target 3: Materials and their properties
Included in this attainment target are the knowledge and understanding of the properties and classification of materials, naturally occurring and manufactured materials, chemical changes and the Earth and its atmosphere.

Attainment target 4: Physical processes
This attainment target includes knowledge and understanding of electricity and magnetism, energy resources and energy transfer, forces and their effects, light and sound, and the Earth's place in the Universe.

Children's attitudes are also important if they are to engage purposefully in scientific activity. The attitudes which need to be developed to produce effective scientific ways of thinking and working include:
• curiosity;
• perseverance;
• critical reflection;

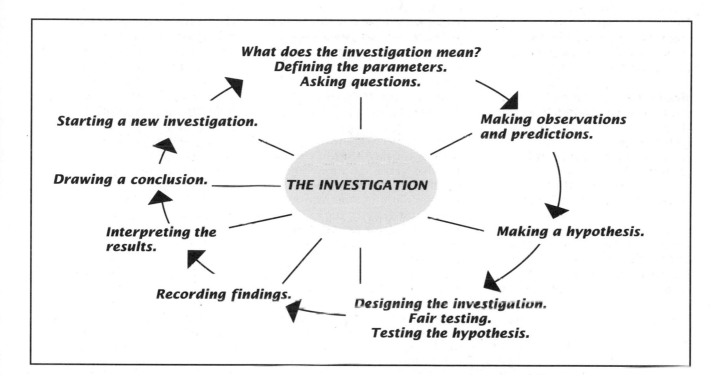

The INVESTIGATION diagram showing the cyclical investigative process:

- What does the investigation mean? Defining the parameters. Asking questions.
- Making observations and predictions.
- Making a hypothesis.
- Designing the investigation. Fair testing. Testing the hypothesis.
- Recording findings.
- Interpreting the results.
- Drawing a conclusion.
- Starting a new investigation.

- open-mindedness;
- appropriately valuing the suggestions of others;
- sensitivity to the living and non-living environment;
- willingness to tolerate uncertainty;
- respect for evidence;
- creativity and inventiveness;
- co-operation with others.

Although this book is concerned with carrying out investigations in science, it is important to emphasise the close relationship of Attainment target 1: Scientific investigation to those attainment targets relating to knowledge and understanding (AT2, 3 and 4). Investigative work should use, reinforce and develop the concepts of science. Knowledge and understanding in science are inextricably linked to scientific investigation and form the contexts for children's investigations. As they carry out their investigations they will develop a deeper understanding of scientific concepts.

There are a number of stages in the investigative process which are best thought of in terms of a cyclical process as shown above.

This book is concerned with helping children to develop the investigative skills which form part of the above cycle. The book shows how to link these skills together and to place these investigations in different contexts which will increase scientific knowledge and understanding.

What is in this book for you?

This book aims to increase the confidence and competence of primary teachers to help children develop an enquiring, investigative approach to science, enabling them to carry out whole investigations. Development of scientific skills which enable children to ask questions, predict, plan, carry out, record, communicate and interpret the results of scientific investigations is an essential part of this process. These skills and their progression are individually analysed in

Chapters 2–7. Chapter 1 discusses the development of investigative skills using different teaching and learning strategies.

Chapters 8–19 consider a number of investigations. These are grouped together through topics/themes which are commonly taught in primary schools. Each chapter describes six investigative activities and one whole investigation. The six investigative activities identify and develop skills from mainly one strand of AT1, thus preparing children to independently plan, carry out and evaluate whole investigations which develop and compile investigative skills from each of the three strands identfied in AT1. The activities within each chapter have been written for use in the primary school and specialised equipment is only used where necessary. The activities cover both Key Stages 1 and 2.

Each activity identifies the appropriate key stage, but the children's ability and prior experience are more important than their age when selecting activities. The teacher's knowledge of the children is of vital importance. Group size is also very important and suggestions are made for this, based on the nature of the activity. A major part of each activity is a set of 'What to do' guidelines. Examples of questions to ask and ways of recording the children's work are also given, and may be modified as appropriate to suit the teacher's needs. Another important feature is the science content of the activity. Many teachers have little or no science background and this information is intended to help teachers in this situation to develop confidence in dealing with science. Finally, many of the activities include ideas for further study and advice on safety in the classroom.

Each chapter is introduced with a topic web which clearly shows the activities included in the chapter. A grid is also provided which relates AT1: Scientific investigation levels, programmes of study and statements of attainment, to the individual activities described in the chapters.

Chapter 20 offers advice on assessment and recording of children's achievements in scientific investigations. Some helpful addresses of educational organisations which will provide materials, posters and information for primary science investigations can be found in Chapter 21.

Finally, there is a useful set of photocopiable sheets which relate directly to particular activities and will save time in the busy primary classroom.

As a whole, the book is designed for primary teachers to help children carry out investigations which develop an increasing knowledge and understanding of science, an approach which must begin in the primary school.

CHAPTER 1

Developing investigation skills in primary schools

Children carry out investigations from a very early age, although at first these are relatively unsophisticated. For instance, a toddler may in the process of turning over a brick or log notice that there are a large number of creepy-crawlies (animals) underneath. She may even notice that there are a number of different kinds of creepy-crawlies. The child moves to the next brick or log with a question in her mind which is probably coupled with a prediction. There is an expectation that there will be creepy-crawlies under the next log and a view (prediction) that there will be as many. The child turns over the log, is disappointed and says 'not many under there', and wanders off. This child has clearly carried out an investigation where a question has been raised, a test has been undertaken and a conclusion has been reached. It is this natural curiosity of many young children that makes investigation such a fruitful avenue of study, during which scientific concepts and language will develop hand in hand with a growing sophistication in scientific investigative skills.

BACKGROUND

The simple investigation carried out by the toddler mirrors the process through which teachers are encouraged to investigate in the classroom. Attainment target 1: Scientific investigation suggests that pupils should:

'... develop the intellectual and practical skills which will allow them to explore and investigate the world of science and develop a fuller understanding of scientific phenomena, the nature of the theories explaining these, and the procedures of scientific investigation. This should take place through activities that require a progressively more systematic and quantified approach which develops and draws upon an increasing knowledge and understanding of science. The activities should encourage the ability to plan and carry out investigations in which pupils:
i) ask questions, predict and hypothesise;
ii) observe, measure and manipulate variables;
iii) interpret their results and evaluate scientific evidence.'

Details of the programmes of study at Key Stages 1 and 2, may be consulted in *Science in the National Curriculum* (1991). Whilst it is not possible to discuss these stages in great detail here, some of the key lines of progression can be identified briefly. These are outlined in the table below:

Key Stage 1	Key Stage 2
Asking questions, suggesting ideas, making predictions.	Moving towards formulation of testable hypotheses.
Appreciating the need for safe and careful action.	Understanding and practising safety and care.
Introducing the idea of a fair test.	Involving identification and manipulation of variables including those to be controlled in fair tests.
Mainly qualitative in approach.	Increasingly more quantitative in approach.
Using non-standard measures (for example, hand spans) and standard measures.	Developing skills in using equipment and measurement; making decisions about when, what and how to measure.
Using data bases such as 'Our Facts' to record similarities and differences observed during sorting activities.	Capture, transmission, storage and retrieval of information using computers and sensors.
Understanding the purposes of recording results; systematic recording using appropriate methods, for example, block graphs and frequency charts.	Systematically listing and recording data, for example, frequency tables and bar charts.
Encouraging interpretation of results.	Searching for patterns in data; interpreting data and evaluating validity of conclusions.
Questioning what they have done and suggesting improvements.	Appraising their investigations and suggesting improvements to methods.

But how may the investigative skills detailed in the programmes of study and statements of attainment be introduced to children? How may the lines of progression within the three strands be developed? Is one approach the answer or can numerous approaches be adopted? This chapter, and those that follow it, offer answers to these questions and practical assistance to teachers in the classroom.

Investigative skills

These may be developed through five main approaches:
1. by helping children to develop specific skills, such as, measuring and recording;
2. by using published work-cards which illustrate good practice in specific skills, such as encouraging the children to

look for patterns in results;
3. by teachers demonstrating good practice, by questioning and example, in order to develop skills from one or two of the strands of AT1, with children concentrating on the other(s);
4. by pupils carrying out whole investigations on their own;
5. by teacher inputs during 2–4 above.

1. Developing individual skills through teaching

Progress in reaching competency in investigations will not be attained if children do not have the necessary individual skills. It might lead also to the development of incorrect notions of concepts. For example, children will be

prevented from gaining accurate data on temperature differences if they cannot read a thermometer, and might conclude that the temperature of the water was colder than that of the air on a frosty morning if they cannot read the instrument correctly.

These individual skills must be taught from an early age and over-learning (where the skill is practised and practised until competency is assured) is important. Opportunities to practise individual skills during whole investigations may not be sufficient and more concentrated practice and teaching may be necessary, such as written or

silver and gold certificates depending on the number of skills achieved.

better still, practical examples. This may be resisted by some teachers who would argue that a real context is always necessary. Such views need challenging because, if there are relatively few opportunities afforded by real contexts and this leads to a lack of competency, the confidence of the child is undermined and the ability to carry out investigations is reduced. This 'catch-22' situation needs to be addressed somewhere and frequency of opportunity through concentrated training at the right time offers the most promising route to competency for most children. The development of such skills supports activities in other curriculum areas, such as mathematics, geography and technology. Teachers might like to consider developing a Skills List Checklist appropriate to the age and ability of their pupils which could be presented in the form of a certificate. This could be done either by listing the skills in which competency has been shown or by awarding bronze,

2. Using published schemes and workcards

Many workcards and published schemes demonstrate good practice in developing individual, and groups of, scientific investigative skills. But the teacher must beware. Some of the earlier schemes tend to be very prescriptive by selecting the questions for the children to investigate, telling them how to carry out a fair test and which materials and instruments to use. Thus, for example, the setting up of a fair test could be learned implicitly by the child, though it is unlikely that many did so because they were not asked frequently to think and reason for themselves how to do it, which variables to control and which variables to measure. However, many workcard schemes are particularly strong in getting children to record their results in a variety of ways and to consider the interpretations of their results. These may be more helpful in providing children with the basic skills to carry out their own investigations.

Recent science schemes generally have been more balanced in their approach, reflecting the nature of science and its role in the National Curriculum.

3. Teacher-led inputs during investigations

At the start of this chapter we discussed how children investigate, though be it in an unsophisticated way, from a very early age. Gradually that sophistication develops as various teaching strategies are applied and children's mental capacity increases. We believe that there is a need for teachers to teach children, somewhat formally, key features of investigative work as one of the ways to move towards higher achievement. As well as the other teaching strategies used, we recommend that the teacher plays a key role by making large inputs into one aspect (one strand for convenience) of children's investigative work. For example, during work on the human body in a topic entitled 'Ourselves', the children might be considering pulse rates and heart beat rates. The teacher could lead an input aimed at raising questions which could be tested, making predictions and suggesting how the investigation may be carried out (see Figure 1). The children would be encouraged to ask questions such as 'Does the heart beat change?', or 'Is the heart beat faster than the pulse rate?' at their own level. The teacher would then help the children to put their questions in a form which could be investigated and help them to make predictions and to suggest ways of carrying out the test. In this way help is given, good practice is employed and the teachers

Teacher-led input	Children's responses
Children raise questions at *teacher's* suggestion.	'Does the number of heart beats change?'
Teacher asks when might heart beat change.	'On a warm/cold day?' 'After exercise?'
Children *guided* to make a prediction in a form which may be investigated.	'After exercise the number of heart beats will increase.'
Teacher helps children to consider/remember from previous work why this might be.	'More blood is needed by the body during exercise.'
Teacher helps children to relate their prediction to knowledge gained during the topic of 'Ourselves', thus making it a hypothesis.	'The number of heart beats will increase after exercise because more blood is needed by the body/muscles.'

Figure 1

have used their time productively and efficiently.

The original question is now in a form which may be investigated, and a hypothesis has been made which is related to prior knowledge. The teacher could then ask the children for ideas on how they might try to verify their hypothesis, before asking them to carry out a fair test and record and interpret their results. Similarly, the teacher would have a major input into a different aspect (strand) of later investigations with the children having a major input with the other two (see the table below).

Strand 1	Strand 2	Strand 3
Teacher-led	Children carry out	Children carry out
Children carry out	**Teacher-led**	Children carry out
Children carry out	Children carry out	**Teacher-led**

Ourselves
When does the heart beat change?
Is the heart beat faster than the pulse rate?

The advantages of this more 'formal' approach is that the children are given a framework on which to carry out future investigations. They have talked about, exchanged ideas and carried out aspects of good practice controlled by the teacher. However, they are not passive onlookers but are involved in the decisions which are skilfully orchestrated by the teacher. These inputs are also efficient in terms of teaching and learning because they could involve a relatively large number of children, even the whole class, at the discretion of the teacher.

4. Children's whole investigations

Children should be given opportunities to carry out whole investigations during which they raise a question, make a prediction or hypothesis, plan and carry out their fair tests, record and interpret their results, make conclusions, relate these to their original hypotheses and, if appropriate, evaluate the validity of the evidence on which their findings were made. This is, of course, not to say that the teacher does not have a role. The teacher will be talking to the children, helping them to ask questions, asking them if they have carried out a fair test, helping them to record and display their results and interacting with the children whenever possible, or providing assistance if required. However, the 'ownership' of, and responsibility for the investigation rests with the children, and they should be encouraged to make decisions initially, even if these are modified through discussions with the teacher.

5. Teacher inputs

Methods 2–4 require inputs from teachers if investigative skills are to develop successfully. Children will ask for assistance when they are having difficulties, but children are not always aware, for example, when they have carried out a fair test, when they are using a measuring instrument incorrectly, or when they are not displaying their results in the most appropriate way. Teacher inputs at these moments are most important.

By using the variety of strategies and methods discussed in this chapter, children's investigative skills will develop along with their knowledge and understanding of science.

CHAPTER 2

Observing

Newly born babies begin to observe their surroundings immediately. They soon begin to explore using one or more of their senses of sight, hearing, touch, taste and smell. Through use of these senses, observational skills begin to develop and continue to develop. The extent of this, however, will depend on the passive or active role of the observer and the degree to which observational skills are given prominence in teaching and learning. Observation is an important process skill of scientific investigation and should be given emphasis and status in the classroom from an early age. But what is observation and how might observational skills be developed?

Dictionary definitions of 'observe' might include 'notice', 'watch' or 'note systematically'. These definitions offer different insights into the nature of observation, for while 'notice' and particularly 'watch' suggest a rather passive interaction, 'note systematically' suggests strongly a more active pursuit which is central to sound scientific observation. While observational skills may be enhanced through teaching and the introduction of motivating activities, the quality of observations will depend on a number of factors including the context of the observation and the experiences of the observer as we shall see later.

BACKGROUND

The 1991 version of *Science in the National Curriculum* offers at first glance little emphasis on the skill or process of observing. The word 'observe' is mentioned explicitly in Attainment target 1: Scientific investigation, in Strand (ii), entitled, 'observe, measure and manipulate variables'. However, direct references to 'observe' or 'observation' are not to be found in the programmes of study at either Key Stage 1 or 2. This is, on the face of it, surprising, particularly if children are to be given practical experiences at the beginning of a new piece of work where they interact with materials, make observations about these materials and then ask questions, make predictions and suggest hypotheses.

Clearly, observation is important when children ask questions such as 'Why didn't it light up?' or 'What will happen if I push it harder?' Observation as a key investigative skill is further illustrated by children in responding to, for example, a question such as 'Do magnets attract (stick to) all objects?' and when they point out (predict) that a magnet will attract a key because it is shiny. Thus, questions may not be asked appropriately and predictions and hypotheses cannot be made sensibly as suggested in Attainment target 1, Strand (i) ('Ask questions, predict and hypothesise'), without careful observations. This is in addition to children being able to 'observe, measure and manipulate

variables', as stated in Strand (ii) of Attainment target 1. Here, children will be observing closely their investigations employing their senses, using their sight to measure accurately quantities, and considering the variables (factors) which might affect their results. Children also need to be accurate and thoughtful in their observations if they are to 'interpret their results and evaluate scientific evidence' as stated in Strand (iii) of Attainment target 1.

In short, observation is an integral part of science and scientific investigation. It is not a low-level skill which is easily mastered, but a complex process involving the use of the senses where perceptions are selected, made sense of and related to prior experiences. The development of observational skills

Objects attracted by the magnet

continues throughout schooling and perhaps throughout life because it requires experience, motivation and mental interaction to lead to refinement. This is reflected in Attainment target 1: Scientific investigation, of the science National Curriculum explicitly but also, and more important, implicitly. Questions and hypotheses cannot be made without observations, accurate measurements may not be made without careful attention to instrumentation, patterns in results could not be perceived and criticism of the methods used and results so obtained could not be offered without observational skills.

This complex nature of observing and observations is summarised on page D12 of the *Non- Statutory Guidance of the Science National Curriculum* (DES 1989). 'Observation is the process by which:
• perceptions are *selected*
• perceptions are *interpreted*
• perceptions' significance are judged against *experience and understanding*'.

It is therefore clear that observation overlaps all other investigative skills and ranges from the passive to being very active mentally. Thus, the mental demand of direct observations such as measuring and observing differences is generally less than the indirect, more abstract observation of identifying variables and interpreting data.

Research on observational skills

Assessment of observational skills in written form has been difficult to carry out as indicated by research from the Assessment of Performance Unit (APU). It considered that many question types assessed language or prior knowledge and not observational skills. Even the assessment of scientific drawings of objects such as sycamore wings was considered not to be totally appropriate because the '...assessment was not of the observations themselves but of their representation in the form of the drawings' (Russell, Black, Bell and Daniels, 1991). This therefore left them with two broad categories of questions:
• observing and communicating similarities and differences between objects, photographs and events;
• making generalisations about their observed similarities and differences' (page 14, Russell et al., 1991).

Trials in schools using questions derived from these categories yielded the following results and conclusions.
'• Scientific concepts held by pupils interact with their skills of observation and so influence performance.
• Performance is influenced by the content and context of the questions. This means that the process of observation should be learned in as broad a range of contexts as possible, using various objects and events to minimise the effect of these features on pupil performance.
• Individuals do not perform in a consistent way across different questions, so it is questionable whether or not they can be said to have a generalised skill of observing similarities and differences.
• In the surveys, the observation of *differences* by pupils at ages ll and 13 was consistently better than their

observation of *similarities*. Opportunities to practise both are needed when pupils are developing their observation skills.

• The observations recorded by pupils are often lacking in detail and much less in number than that expected or possible. Observation is common in science lessons, but it is loosely defined and consequently lacks focus. Demands need to be made clear in extent and nature, with the need for repeated observations for checking being emphasised.

• Pupils should be taught the reason for quantified observations...though pupils obviously *can* and *do* measure if asked to, the vast majority do not if left to decide for themselves.

• The purpose of the observations should be revealed to the pupils.

• Teaching should include opportunities for pupils to generate their own classes, using both everyday and "scientific" items.

• Assessment tasks need to be varied and selected carefully, with particular attention being paid to content, the context, the question demand, and the number and complexity of the possible observations.'
(Russell et al., 1991)

These research findings illustrate once again the complexity of observation and perhaps point to a need to sub-divide the skill of observation much more. For example, the authors of the *Age 11 APU Report* [DES (1988)] had great difficulty in constructing questions to assess the skill of *measurement* as distinct from *observation*. Indeed, they conclude that measurement was a different kind of observation 'having external and quantified criteria' (p 103).

This research is also useful when considering how to help children to improve their observational skills.

Improving the quality of observations

We mentioned briefly that the context and demand of an investigation and the prior experiences of the investigator will affect the quality of observations. For example, while the senses may interact passively with all the information in front of a child, this information will be selected depending on the interests, experience and conceptual understanding of a child. Thus the chosen information may not be that which the teacher expected the child to gather. Furthermore, the many observations which it is possible to make, for example, when looking at a burning candle, may distract and confuse the child from the main focus of the activity which might be to observe the wax melting and solidifying. Children may be helped in their observations if they:

• understand the nature of a question and the purpose of their observations, possibly through game-like activities;

• are helped to identify the relevant from the 'irrelevant' observations;

• are given a framework in which to observe, for example, starting at the top of an object and working down;

• appreciate that observations involve all the senses (but that smell and taste must be carefully used), as there is evidence that children under-use their senses;

• are given time to make detailed observations;

• are helped by teacher interaction to focus the

observation from the superficial to the detailed;
• are allowed to express their own individuality through an open-ended element to the observation;
• are asked to look for similarities as well as differences;
• are encouraged to look for detail as well as the main features;
• have omitted detail pointed out to them by questioning (see Chapter 3);
• are encouraged to draw, label and annotate drawings;
• are able to compare and discuss their observations;
• are provided with stimulating material from a variety of contexts;
• see that observing will raise questions which may be investigated.

Quality of observation

The quality or precision of children's observations other than for measurement and for grouping of animals in Attainment target 2, Strand (ii), is implicit rather than explicit in the National Curriculum. Therefore, the teacher must endeavour to show a progression of detail and precision in the classroom through careful selection of activities and through high, but realistic expectations.

We are reminded of an excellent example of observation during a visit to a local farm during work on 'Food and Farming'. 'What colour is that cow?' asked the farmer, underestimating the abilities of the children. 'It is black and white on *this side*', beamed a small girl. This could have been a relatively passive observation, but the child ensures that it is linked with an internal interaction, involving the tentativeness of scientific evidence indicating the ability to make no more of the evidence that is revealed through observation or investigation.

Another example of a quality observation involved children mixing red cabbage juice/water with a variety of household, aqueous solutions when beginning work on acid, alkaline and neutral solutions. Most of the class were making observations such as 'It's gone red' or 'It is purple', when one boy responded to my question in a thoughtful way: 'It is mainly purple, red on the surface and pinkish in between; I only added one drop but I am going to add some more'. This boy was not content with a quick look at

the overall situation but was looking for detail and accuracy. These types of detailed observations should be encouraged.

The purpose of observations

Helping children to observe has a number of purposes because:
• it encourages curiosity;
• observing similarities and differences leads to the development of classification skills and to the identification and manipulation of variables;
• observing events and sequences leads to conceptual development, for example, in learning about the transition from tadpole to frog;
• it develops knowledge;
• it acts as a stimulus to investigative work;
• by observing patterns in observations, children are helped towards interpreting their work and making conclusions.

Some of these purposes of careful observation are illustrated in the example activity on the next page.

How are we the same; how are we different?

Age range
Key Stage 2.

Group size
Individuals or pairs.

What you need
Pond animals or land 'minibeasts', white trays, plastic containers with lids, teaspoons, hand lenses or magnifiers.

What to do
After the children have observed the animals for some time, suggest that they look closely at two animals from the same classification group, such as a slug and a snail (molluscs) or a freshwater shrimp and a water louse (crustaceans). The children should be encouraged to draw large detailed pictures of the two animals. Similarities and differences could be recorded by annotating the diagrams or by the use of tables.

Next, let the children examine animals from different classification groups, such as a water louse (crustacean) and a damselfly nymph (insect). Again, they should record any similarities and differences using annotated diagrams or tables.

Investigative skills
The children may have made a series of related observations and may have quantified the length of the animals using a ruler. They might have noticed that some animals swim while other crawl and these observations might lead them to ask questions, make predictions and design investigations.

Content
This activity gives children the opportunity to identify similarities and differences, both within a group of animals and between groups of animals. Through activities like this, children will be helped to understand the principles on which classification systems are built. The activity might help to develop their concept of an insect (three pairs of legs) and a crustacean (more than four pairs of legs) and to realise that these all belong to the class of arthropods (class: Arthropoda), which have jointed legs and a body divided into three parts.

Further activity
Repeat the activity, but use different pond animals, minibeasts obtained from under stones, grass sweeps or by tree shaking, or plants.

AT1/2b,3b; AT2/2b,4b

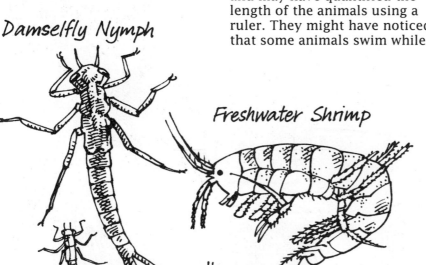

Damselfly Nymph

real size

Freshwater Shrimp

real size

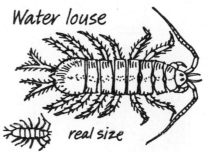

Water louse

real size

CHAPTER 3

Asking questions, predicting and hypothesising

In a classroom where successful investigative work is being undertaken, an observer would hear the sound of discussions, equipment being collected and assembled, see the interest and excitement on children's faces and witness their novel testing strategies, but would also be aware of the number of questions being asked by both teacher and children. It is these questions, coupled with observations and prior experience, that are vital to the starting point for investigations. In this chapter we will look at teachers' questions and children's questions, predictions and hypotheses, individually, but will highlight the important links between them.

BACKGROUND

Teachers' questions

Elstgeest (1985) identified six categories of 'productive' questions which are listed and discussed below:
- attention-focusing questions;
- measuring and counting questions;
- comparison questions;
- action questions;
- problem-posing questions;
- how and why (reasoning) questions.

   Successful and appropriate use of these types of question by the teacher will gradually lead to purposeful questioning by the children, to predictions being made based on experience, to predictions being made with a rationale based on scientific knowledge and, ultimately, to hypotheses where the causal link is rooted in scientific knowledge, understanding and theory.

Attention-focusing questions

Questions should, if possible, stimulate involvement and curiosity, encouraging children to observe more closely and deeply. As they explore new materials, objects and organisms, 'Have you noticed...?' types of questions will help to focus their attention and should encourage a response such as 'Yes, there are six of them and they are hairy.' This might well be followed by an exploratory phase with little direction from the teacher. The 'What is it?', 'What does it do?' type questions (Elstgeest, 1985) are then more likely to be raised by the children.

Measuring and counting questions

'How long?', 'How many?' and 'What is the temperature ...?' are the type of questions asked in this category and the children may be able to approach them with confidence if their skills of measurement are relatively sophisticated (see Chapter 5). There is a progression in learning from non-standard units to standard units, initially using simple instruments to the nearest labelled division, but later using more complicated instruments and finer divisions. This is the beginning of the quantification of variables in investigations. The advice of Elstgeest (1985) that '... no teacher can challenge your (the children's) measuring ruler', cannot, surely, be defended for the skills of measurement should be refined through questioning, checking and teaching.

Comparison questions

Measurement and counting questions naturally lead on to comparison questions such as 'Is it longer?', 'Does it weigh as much? or 'Are there as many?' However, not all comparison questions need to be quantitative, as Elstgeest (1985) points out. Young children studying fruits or seeds might be asked questions such as 'Are they the same colour?', 'Are they the same shape?' or 'Do they smell the same?' Older children could be asked a more open comparison question such as 'Tell me how your fruits are similar and how they are different?', where the question is not sub-divided. As well as emphasising the basis for classification, the teacher is highlighting (by questioning) the variables in fruits. Some of these are easily divided into 'red fruit' or 'green fruit' categories (categoric variables) while others are different sizes (continuous variables). Through these types of questions children's early perceptions of variables are developed.

Action questions

'What happens if...?' questions will be followed up by investigation, a result and subsequent discussion. Examples could include:
• 'What happens if you place the car higher up the ramp?'
• 'What happens if we put the plants in the dark?'
• 'What happens if we put the sugar in warmer water?'
This question type helps children make sense of their experience and, if generalised, adds to their conceptual understanding that vehicles go further if released further up the slope, that plants grow long, leggy and yellow in the

dark and that sugar dissolves more quickly in warmer water. It also motivates and encourages curiosity and investigation.

Problem-posing questions

Following experience with the materials or equipment discussed in the questions above, children will be able to respond to 'Can you find a way to...?' questions. Predictions will be made based on this experience and investigations will be carried out to attempt to verify the prediction. This type of question helps children to frame investigations of their own and to begin to carry out fair tests as a result, though the latter will need separate, more focused inputs. Further examples might include:
• 'Can you find a way to make your vehicle go even further/ across the room?'
• 'Can you find out whether woodlice prefer a damp or a dry home?'

How and why (reasoning) questions

These 'How do you think it happened?' and more importantly 'Why do you think it happened?' questions ask children to reason about their

experiences, to interpret their results and to make conclusions. There is evidence to suggest that these questions are asked parsimoniously in classrooms. This might be because children enjoy investigating but are far less keen to interpret their findings, because they find consideration of the implications of their results difficult, or that teachers are uncertain about the appropriate interpretation themselves, or a combination of these factors. Whatever is the case, the importance of these type of questions should not be underestimated because they help children to consider the relationships they have uncovered and relate these to their original prediction or hypothesis. If the question is posed as 'Why do you *think* it happened?' rather than 'Why did it happen?', a more open discussion will develop where different viewpoints will be considered, analysed, and possibly discarded while others are retained. Gradually, with repetition and encouragement, children will start to interpret their findings automatically.

Children's questions

The most important aspect of encouraging children to ask questions must be for the teacher to establish a conducive atmosphere. This may be achieved in two main ways:
• responding positively to questions;
• possessing a flexible view of science as a changing body of knowledge, at least in terms of children's learning.

Responding positively to questions

Children must be made to feel able to ask a number of questions as long as they are sensible and appropriate and this should stem from an atmosphere where observation, first-hand experience and curiosity are encouraged. A child raising three predictions which could be tested should be considered just as worthy as a child raising one prediction which elucidates the information or relationship the teacher was hoping to establish, at least in terms of asking questions and suggesting ideas.

Possessing a flexible view of science

Science is often viewed as a factual subject, which indeed it is, but this knowledge is continually changing. For instance, early geneticists would be amazed by the discovery of the structure of DNA, and microbiologists and medics who died in the 1970s would be staggered by the Aids phenomenon and the discovery of the HIV virus.

While there is no time for children to discover every bit of scientific knowledge by themselves (even if one thought it possible), and not possible to allow children to follow their own ideas *all* the time, scientific investigations should not be approached with the view that the teacher knows the answer but will not offer it until the children have spent a lot of time reaching a conclusion which is different, and therefore by implication, wrong. 'I do not know, let's find out together', might be a useful underlying philosophy so that questions can be raised and followed up in an open manner. Clearly, however, the teacher must make her/his mind up as to whether a line of investigation has no future, and take appropriate action.

Teachers will be aware that children's questions often concentrate on the known rather than a concern for the unknown. This might stem from the guessing game of 'what my teacher wants me to ask or to answer', but it may be much more than that. This is where the wealth of experience vital to Key Stage 1 and 2 teaching is crucial so that children have concrete experiences on which to ask questions and to follow up ideas. Children's ability to question will also benefit from the purposeful, skilful line of questioning pursued by the teacher (see Teachers' questions, page 22) and the enthusiasm she generates in asking questions and carrying out investigations. It will also be aided by carrying out investigations in which the teacher, albeit with assistance, poses questions and offers predictions based on her knowledge, as a starting point for a fair test to be carried out by the children (this approach is adopted in some of the activities described in Chapters 8–19) of this book). In this way children will be given a role model which they may emulate when they are asked to do the same themselves. Questioning, predicting and hypothesising, like any other skill, need to be taught frequently and in as many ways as possible.

Asking questions, predicting and hypothesising in the National Curriculum

Strand (i) of Attainment target 1: Scientific investigation states that the activities in the classroom should '... encourage the ability to plan and carry out investigations in which pupils: *ask questions, predict and hypothesise*'. The next few pages will indicate with examples the developmental sequence and progression that takes place within KS 1 and 2.

There is no statement of attainment at Level 1 for strand (i) but at Level 2a children should carry out investigations in which they: ' ... ask questions such as "How?", "Why?" and "What will happen if...?", suggest ideas and make predictions.'

Example 1

Investigation: Children may be investigating the melting and solidifying of various substances by heating and cooling. Children could:
Ask questions: Why does chocolate melt in the fingers but not wax? What will happen if we put it on the cooker?
Make predictions: The margarine will melt before the wax which will melt before the chocolate.

At Level 3, children should carry out investigations in which they 'suggest questions, ideas and predictions, based on everyday experience, which can be tested'.

Example 2

Investigation: Children may be investigating the melting and solidifying of various substances. The children handle some wax, jelly and some chocolate and notice that the chocolate begins to melt. Children could:
Suggest questions, ideas and make predictions based on everyday experience: Which will melt first, the jelly or the wax? The chocolate will melt before the wax because it melts in the hand.
Suggest ideas for testing: The jelly and the wax could be put on a tray under the heat to see which one melts first. Alternatively: the wax, jelly and chocolate are put in a separate container each containing a thermometer, floating in a bowl of hot water. We will see at which temperature they begin to melt.

At Level 3, the *children* are suggesting the question to be tested based on their everyday experience. They are also suggesting ideas as to how a test might be carried out and making a prediction about the outcome. The prediction should contain the word 'because' in order to relate it to everyday experience. This is a clear progression from Level 2 where the children have only to ask a question, suggest ideas, and make predictions.

At Level 4, children should carry out investigations in which they '... ask questions, suggest ideas and make predictions, based on some relevant knowledge, in a form which can be investigated'.

Example 3

Investigation: Children are asked to investigate the melting of chocolate, wax and jelly. Children could:
Ask questions, suggest ideas and make predictions based on prior knowledge: Consider that chocolate will melt before wax and jelly because it needs less heat to melt it.
Suggest ideas for testing in a form which can be investigated: The children could suggest melting equal-sized pieces of chocolate, wax and jelly on a tin over a radiator

The progression from Level 3 to Level 4 is obtained in two

ways. Firstly, at Level 4, the child's question, ideas or prediction are based on relevant prior knowledge while at Level 3 these are based on experience. In terms of the melting investigation, children will know from *experience* that chocolate melts in their hands and wax does not, but actual *knowledge* is needed to say that less heat is required to melt chocolate than wax or jelly. The second element of progression involves the actual testing or investigation of the question. At Level 3 the question should be 'in a form which can be investigated'. This subtle wording is open to interpretation but there is a suggestion that questions at Level 4 must be capable of investigation in the school environment, unlike those at Level 3 which could be tested, but not necessarily with the resources available. It should also be noted that while the question/prediction should be based on prior knowledge, this does not have to be scientific knowledge (see Level 5).

At Level 5, children should carry out investigations in which they: '... formulate hypotheses where the causal link is based on scientific knowledge, understanding or theory'.

Example 4
Investigation: To determine what affects the speed at which chocolate melts. Children could:
Formulate hypotheses:
Suggest that temperature is important to the melting of chocolate. The higher the temperature, the quicker it will melt. There is a causal link based on scientific knowledge, understanding or theory because the more heat (energy) there is, the more

quickly it will change from a solid to a liquid, as the molecules heat up and move further apart.

At Level 5, children are asked to produce a hypothesis where the causal link is based on scientific knowledge, understanding or theory – a clear progression from Level 4 when the prediction is based on relevant prior knowledge.

A hypothesis can be considered as a supposition made as a basis for reasoning and investigation. Thus it matters not whether the hypothesis is verified or not, as information is gained whichever is the case. At Level 5 a hypothesis should include the *cause* such as in the example above, 'The higher the temperature, the quicker it will melt' and the effect (because) 'the more quickly it will change from a solid to a liquid as the molecules heat up and move apart', which is based on knowledge, understanding and theory. Children should be encouraged to include the word *because* in any hypothesis and prediction if possible.

While not within the remit of Key Stage 2 teaching, at Level 6, children should carry out investigations in which they: '... use scientific knowledge or theory to predict relationships between continuous variables'.

Example 5
Investigation: Consider the factors that affect the speed at which chocolate melts. Children could:
Predict relationships between continuous variables: Suggest that the higher the temperature the more quickly the chocolate will melt because:

Based on scientific knowledge, understanding or theory:
The more heat energy there is, the more quickly it will change from a solid to a liquid.

Progression between Levels 5 and 6 is achieved by using continuous variables and by predicting the relationship between the variables.

We can now be in no doubt about the close relationship which exists within science, as reflected in the National Curriculum, between scientific investigation and science knowledge and theory. For too long the two have tended to be taught and learned in isolation or one has taken priority over the other. However, while questions, predictions and hypotheses raised without thought such as 'It will be hot tomorrow.' or 'This object will travel faster than that one.' are valid in themselves as they can be tested, they are of far more value if they are based on experience or knowledge. Thus, an investigation on a particular topic cannot be carried out successfully say, at Level 3, 4 or 5 (e.g. on the effect of the amount of water or temperature on decay), unless children have the necessary experience, relevant prior knowledge, or scientific knowledge, understanding or theory respectively, of the key factors in the process of decay (AT2/5d), on which to base a prediction or hypothesis. This does not necessarily mean that children will approach or achieve at one or two levels below that of the knowledge and understanding on which the investigation is based, but this is inevitable unless they have been introduced to the appropriate experiences, knowledge and scientific understanding beforehand.

CHAPTER 4

Fair testing/manipulating variables

Of all the skills associated with scientific investigation, fair testing is probably the one that has little or no place in other areas of the curriculum and is therefore unique to science. Children observe and measure in other disciplines, though perhaps not with the same regularity and intensity. In history children interpret evidence and evaluate their findings. In science and other curriculum areas, questioning and predicting is carried out. Children also hypothesise in science, where the causal link is based on knowledge. This investigation skill, while having its own rigour and identity in science, can also be applied to the humanities subjects and is therefore not as unique to science as fair testing, the manipulation of variables and the carrying out of investigations to obtain meaningful results.

The notion of fair testing and manipulating variables brings a rigour to scientific work which may be unsurpassed in classroom pedagogy. The collection and analysis of historical evidence is similar, but involves more value judgements and does not involve rigorous testing, except against other people's opinions, as does its scientific counterpart. It is this rigour which brings about difficulties in the classroom, because the identification and manipulation of variables while sometimes being concrete, may often involve abstract experiences and deep mental thought. Nevertheless, this rigour brings about much of the fun in science and a liberation within the subject, because children investigate and find out their own 'new' information, with constraints then being placed on equipment rather than methodology.

So how can we help children to develop fair testing skills? How might we help them to understand variables and apply them in investigations and what steps are important on the road to competency? This chapter explores these issues and makes suggestions to help teachers having difficulties with this area, including examples of activities which help to develop fair testing skills.

BACKGROUND

The terminology of variables

Let us first consider an 'everyday' situation where scientific investigation may be used to give us more systematic information about a problem. You have noticed that your white shirts, blouses or T-shirts do not seem as clean as they should be and you are eager to see if a different washing power will help. You purchase two new washing powders and with your usual brand have three to test. You have already asked a question, 'Which is the best washing powder?' and have already identified what you want to find out (the *independent variable*). You now plan your fair test. You might decide to wait until you had three shirts, three blouses and three T-shirts to wash (six

of each would be better) and have therefore identified your sample for the investigation. But how will you know which is the best washing powder when all the washing comes out of the three washes? You decide to give each member of the family a 'vote', by judging the whiteness of the wash: 3 for the best, 2 for the next best and 1 for the worst. The washing powder gaining the highest marks will be judged the best. You have now decided upon the outcome of interest to you which is judged or measured in the investigation (the *dependent variable*), though you might have preferred some more quantitative and less subjective measurement, but acknowledge that this is not available to you. You put one shirt, one blouse and one T-shirt into the wash but before you start you realise that you must make it a fair test by

controlling other factors (variables) which will make the results of the investigation valid. The garments are of equal dirtiness and age, you are going to use one full scoop of washing powder with each wash, the temperature of the water will be the same (40°C, because all the powders wash best at low temperature), the wash cycle will be the same and you will dry them in the same way and for the same length of time. You have now identified the *control variables* and the washing machine may be switched on. You have carried out a fair test though a few questions need to be considered, such as, should you have weighed the powder rather than used a fixed volume and does the use of different garments make it confusing when interpreting the results.

You find out that powder B is the best, but the fair testing bug has really got you now. You want to find out how much powder is needed to

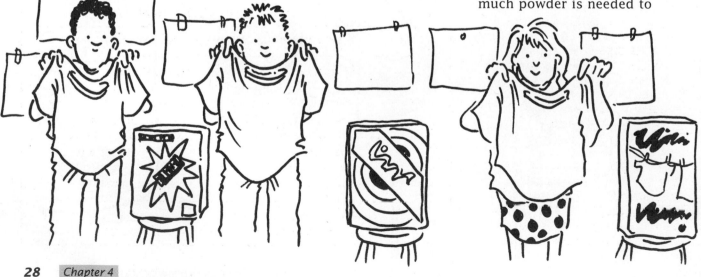

give the best results without waste and whether the optimum temperature is really 40°C. You now have to consider the *range, number* and *value* of your variables. You might decide on a temperature *range* from 20°C to 60°C, the *number* of different temperatures being five and having *values* of 20°C, 30°C, 40°C, 50°C and 60°C, evenly spaced between the smallest and the largest. You have also found out that some variables are *discontinuous*, for example washing powders. Others can have any value and are *continuous*, for example, weight, volume, length, and temperature. Others are *discrete*, having whole numbers only, such as the number of germinated seeds or the number of layers of insulation on a drinks can. However, continuous variables such as temperature may also be treated as having *discrete* values, such as hot and cold. Some variables are said to be *categoric* (the colour of a flower (red/yellow), or the presence or absence of an item such as pips (with pips/ without pips)). Some variables (*derived variables*) need to be calculated from more than one measurement as is the case for the speed of a vehicle travelling down a slope. You have now found out all you need to know about variables but the children will not need to know all these terms, though we will be suggesting that some are very useful to remember and understand,

particularly as they reach the later stages of, and upper levels associated with, Key Stage 2.

It may seem on the face of it that there is little to fair testing and the manipulation of variables, but it does require fairly sophisticated skills and use of mental processes. The demand differs depending on the investigation, not just because of the context, but because of the type of variables that have to be manipulated as determined by the original question. For example, children find continuous variables more difficult to handle than categoric (type of washing powder) or discrete (hot and cold) variables (Strang, Daniels and Bell, 1991). The way in which a child manipulates variables and the strategies he uses will depend on the conceptual understanding that he brings to bear when carrying out a

particular task. Likewise, the context of an investigation may help children remember previous experiences and work which aids planning and the detail of planning. Thus the same child may perform better on one task than another even though the procedural (experimental) demands are similar (Strang, Daniels and Bell, 1991). We will come back later to the demands of investigations posed by the number and type of variables, but firstly we will look at how we may develop an appreciation of fair testing.

Manipulating variables (fair testing) and the National Curriculum

The statements of attainment relating to manipulating variables in *Science in the National Curriculum* (1991) are shown below alongside the appropriate levels of attainment.

Level	Statements of Attainment
1	Observe familiar materials and events.
2	Make a series of related observations.
3	Observe closely and quantify by measuring using appropriate instruments.
4	Carry out a fair test in which they select and use appropriate instruments to measure quantities such as volume and temperature.
5	Choose the range of each of the variables involved to produce meaningful results.

Element of progression	Nature of progression	
Context	Set in everyday, familiar contexts: ———→ 1 the home 2 the playground 3 the shops	Set in new and increasingly unfamiliar contexts: 1. the laboratory 2. the factory 3. the hospital
Variables to be changed (independent) 1 Number	Single: ———————→ 1 guitar string length	Multiple: 1 guitar string length and diameter
2 Type	Categoric: ——————→ 1. colour of car 2. type of material 3. gender	Continuous: 1. length of car 2. mass of material 3. age
Variable(s) to be measured (dependent) Nature	Can be appropriately judged without making measurements: ——→ 1. floating/sinking 2. pitch 3. bendiness	More appropriately measured: _timed process of dissolving._ 1. length 2. temperature 3. voltage
Apparatus	Simple: ——————————→ 1. rulers 2. kitchen scales 3. pipette	Complex: 1. micrometer 2. top pan balance 3. burette
Conceptual burden	Low: ——————————→ Tasks depending on limited understanding or application of particular scientific concepts, eg: *Investigate the extent to which a selection of everyday waste decays naturally.*	High: _Knowledge of the dissolving process._ Tasks depending on increasing understanding or application of particular scientific concepts eg: *Investigate the factors limiting the rate of photosynthesis.*

Table 1

Progression within Attainment target 1

It is not surprising to see a progression of difficulty and complexity running through Attainment target 1 in the context, number and type of variables to be changed, the way in which variables are measured, the apparatus used and the conceptual demand placed on children during an investigation. This is conveniently summarised in Table 1 (Qualter, Strang, Swatton and Taylor, 1990).

Some aspects of Table 1 may be analysed further to relate to levels of attainment, to statements of attainment and to examples of these given in *Science in the National Curriculum* (1991). As the activities given in this section and the examples of statements of attainment given in *Science in the National Curriculum* are for different investigations in different contexts, we feel it is prudent to include here examples from the same investigation but at different levels (see Table 2). In this way, the progression may be appreciated more readily by the non-specialist.

Investigations with sugar and water

Level	Independent variable	Dependent variable	Control variable(s)	Measuring equipment
1	Types of sugar, eg. white and brown, fine and coarse.	Does it disappear (dissolve)?	Not applicable here (but temperature of water, and volume of water).	Judgement by observation.
2	Types of sugar, eg. lump and crystal.	Do they dissolve? Time taken to dissolve (quickly/ slowly).	As above.	Judgement by observation.
3	As above.	Which dissolves more quickly?	Equal volumes of water. Same water temperature. Equal amounts of types of sugar.	Clock/watch to measure time. Water from same tap. Same level in container. One spoonful of sugar.
4	As above. Type of sugar as the variable to be changed.	Which dissolves more quickly? Time as the variable to be measured.	Equal volumes of water. Same water temperature. Equal amounts of types of sugar.	Select clock to measure time. Select measuring cylinder to measure volume. Select thermometer to measure temperature of water or justify equal temperature. Select scales to weigh sugar or justify use of equal spoonfuls.
5	One type of sugar with the temperature of the water in which it is being dissolved being systematically changed.	At what temperature does the sugar dissolve fastest? Time as the variable to be measured.	Equal volumes of water at each temperature. Same amount of sugar at each temperature.	Select clock to measure time. Select measuring cylinder to measure volume. Select thermometer to measure temperature of water. Select scales to weigh sugar.

Table 2

SAMPLE ACTIVITIES

Developing the skills of fair testing (manipulating variables) in the classroom

The skills of fair testing need to be developed from an early age, although the early stages might seem, on the face of it, to have little to do with variables. The initial step, at Level 1, involves children in observing materials, actions and events in familiar situations. However, it is these actions and events which *are* variables and which may be manipulated in later years. This may be seen in the first sample activity. Following a visit to a supermarket the pupils identify simple differences (variables) in the fruits they have brought back to school.

1. Tutti frutti

Age range
Key Stage 1.

Group size
Small groups.

What you need
Fruit from a variety of cultures, cutting board, ruler.

What to do
Ask the children to consider the following questions:
• What is the colour of the fruits? Yellow, green, black, green, red?
• What is the texture of the fruits? Hairy, smooth, rough, pitted?
• What is the shape of the fruits? Round (spherical), long and thin, 'pear-shaped'?
• Are there the same number of seeds in each fruit? Are there a large number of seeds, some seeds, few seeds? How many seeds are there in each fruit?
• Are the seeds the same size? Are some seeds large, medium sized, small? How big (long) are the seeds?
• What do the fruits smell like? Do any of them smell similar?
• What do the fruits taste like? Do any of them taste similar?

Investigative skills
The children have observed familiar fruits (items) in some detail and have discussed ideas about them. They have probably made a number of related observations, comparing the size, shape, smell, taste and number of pips/seeds in the fruits. You and the children have identified a number of simple differences (variables) between the fruits. This will help in designing fair tests later.

Safety
Pupils should be encouraged to taste items only if directed by the teacher.

AT1/1a,2b

Similarly, at Level 2, children might be asked to examine a variety of fabrics and might choose to group them according to texture, dividing them into three sets of 'rough', 'medium' and 'smooth' (AT1/2b). These sets are variables (something subject to variation) of texture and later children might wish to investigate on which of these surfaces a vehicle will travel the furthest.

Another example might involve children making a simple moving vehicle and rolling it down a slope, first with small wheels, then with medium-sized wheels and finally with big wheels. They might observe that it went a long way (10 floor tiles) with the big wheels, a medium distance (8 tiles) with the medium wheels and not very far (4 tiles) with the small wheels (AT1/2b). In this example, like the one on fabrics above, the children are changing one variable (size of wheels) and finding that this affects (varies) the distance (the second variable) travelled by the vehicle, although at Level 2, non-standard units are acceptable. You might like to turn back to earlier in this section and find out which is the dependent and which is the independent variable, though children at this stage do not need to be made aware of it.

By having plenty of practice in identifying differences at an early stage, children will be better placed to identify and control variables and to recognise the fairness of a test later in their development.

Gradually, as children develop their measuring skills

(see Chapter 5), they will be able to quantify variables. This marks an important phase in scientific development, particularly if children are always seeking to quantify their findings. This might indicate a child who is not content with non-standard measures (such as 4 'floor tiles'), an able mathematician or a child who is showing early signs of high ability in science, or all of these qualities. Quantifying variables should be nurtured and developed. Opportunities for measurement are numerous in science as is indicated by the Level 3 example below.

Here, the pupils are encouraged to grow plants from seeds. By doing so, they will be asked to measure a variable such as growth which changes over time.

2. Investigating growth

Age range
Key Stage 1 and 2.

Group size
Pairs.

What you need
Bought plant pots, plastic/polystyrene cups or yogurt cartons with a hole made in the base, cress, pea or bean seeds, seed compost or soil. The seeds could be provided by the school or from 'unused' sources at home. Remember that some varieties of seeds have a short shelf-life and therefore may not germinate.

What to do
Place compost or soil in the containers and plant the seeds following the instructions on the packet.

Measure the growth of the plants on a daily basis either in pictorial form, against a prefixed measuring device or by direct measurement to the appropriate level of accuracy (1cm/0.5cm). Ensure that the children carry out a fair test by measuring from the same point each time (rulers which measure along the whole length of the instrument are preferable to those which have small pieces of wood or plastic without graduations at each end).

Investigative skills
The children have observed and measured carefully using an appropriate instrument (ruler) and should notice that the growth of plants changes over time.

Thus, at the teacher's level, the growth of plants is a simple continuous, dependent variable that changes over time.

Safety
The children should keep their fingers away from their mouths and wash their hands after being in contact with soil or compost.

AT1/3b

Thus, at Level 3, children need to be able to quantify a simple, continuous variable which changes over time as well as taking other discontinuous measurements. Other measuring activities which also involve a simple, continuous variable that changes over time could include the weight of the baby gerbils or guinea pigs, the height of the children during their school life, the temperature of the air at a particular time on a daily basis or the position of the sun. Other measuring activities involving discontinuous measurements could include the temperature of the air, a pond, in a fridge and above a radiator, the volume of rain water produced each day or week, and the weight (mass) of various objects which float or sink (see Chapter 11).

Investigations and practical activities carried out by the teacher should set a good example for children from an early age by ensuring that fair testing is high on the list of priorities. Initially, this will be promoted by the teacher but later more and more by the children, as they begin to realise that investigations may be set up in a 'fair' or 'unfair' manner. This might arise firstly through what the children will see as 'competitive' situations, for example when they are rolling their vehicles down a slope to see which one goes the furthest. 'That's not fair – she's pushing it', or 'That's not fair – he started the vehicle over the line', will indicate that the children are coming to understand more about fair testing, though it may be a long time before they can carry out a fair test competently for themselves. This good practice on the part of the teacher may be shown, for example, when carrying out an activity on the floating and sinking of objects. The teacher will tell the children that they must drop the objects in the water from the same height and in the same way 'to make it fair'. Bad practice would involve dropping from a great height those items which are predicted to sink, and gently lowering into the water those which are predicted to float.

Scientific knowledge may also get in the way of encouraging good practice towards fair testing. We remember being asked by two girls for the weighing scales during an activity on melting and solidifying margarine, chocolate, wax and ice. 'Why do you want the scales?' we enquired. 'To ensure there are equal amounts', said one of them. Conscious that the amount would not affect the way the substances melted or the temperature at which they melted, we hastily said they need not bother. 'But it won't be a fair test', the other girl protested, anxiously. The scales were duly found and evidence of advancing scientific attainment had been shown by the girls if not by ourselves! But it is a lesson we did not forget and it improved our practice in the classroom. The moral of the story is to not let your own knowledge affect the rigour with which the children pursue their scientific investigations.

Children are not asked in the 1991 version of Attainment target 1, Scientific investigation, under strand (ii) entitled 'observe, measure and manipulate variables', to distinguish between a fair test and an unfair test, as was the case in the earlier 1989 version. However, under strand (iii), 'interpret their results and evaluate scientific evidence', they are asked to: '... recognise that their results may not be valid unless a fair test has been carried out'. But what does this statement really mean? It is undoubtedly less demanding for children to identify that some of their friends are not carrying out a fair test and to point out why, than to carry out an investigation, obtain some results and then during reflection realise that conclusions are invalid because a fair test has not been carried out. If young children have carried out an investigation they are not going to be able to spot weaknesses readily in their own methodology without intervention from the teacher. It is perhaps surprising to see this level of demand required at Level 3, a level that bright 7 year olds or average 9/10 year olds might be achieving. However, when one reads the example given to explain the statement in *Science in the National Curriculum* (1991) a somewhat different interpretation is likely: '... show that they understand that the different batches of seeds should be planted at the same time, in similar containers and given the same amount of water'.

This example merely indicates whether the children have carried out a fair test or not and does not make any reference to interpreting results or evaluating scientific evidence. It does not refer in any way to the first few words of the statement of attainment, '... recognise that their conclusions ...' Therefore to all intents and purposes, in our opinion, the statement should be more appropriately placed under '... strand (ii), observing, measuring and manipulating variables' and could read 'distinguish between a "fair" and an "unfair" test' but should mainly involve *categoric* variables (the presence or absence of a feature, for example, light) and not *continuous* variables, (variables which can have any value) for the *independent* variable (variable which is changed) at this stage. However, the *dependent* variable (outcome of interest to the investigator) will be *continuous*. This is implicit within the examples given in the National Curriculum (1991) but nowhere is it *explicit* and so is confusing to teachers. One wonders how many children have been asked to consider investigations involving two continuous variables, when they have not yet mastered one categoric and one continuous variable.

Children might be able to show that they *understand* that a fair test has or has not been carried out if they see that a group next to them are dropping balls from different heights or that certain balls are being pushed and not others, in an investigation designed to find out which ball is the bounciest. Similarly, in an investigation to find out what is needed to help plants to grow, children might notice that the plants in the dark have been given only a drop of water while those in the light have been given much more... 'It's not fair, Miss!'

Alternatively, children might be able to show that they understand that a fair test has been carried out if they are able to point out, after the investigation in response to the question, 'How did you carry out a fair test?', that they dropped, or should have dropped the balls from the same height on to the same piece of floor during the bouncing balls investigation. After completing the growth investigation, the children should be able to say that the plants were planted in similar pots, at the same time, with similar soil and were given the same amount of water. The word *understand* is crucial here, because it suggests to us that at Level 3 the children do not have to actually carry out a fair test (though they will have carried out a test during their investigation), but have to understand how a fair test *could* have been carried out. This could perhaps be under the direction or prompting of the teacher following a question such as 'You have planted the seeds at the same time in similar pots but what

else might you have done to make it fair?', or 'What could you have done with the water to make your investigation fairer, John?' It is thus active in mental terms but may be passive in terms of actually carrying out the fair test.

At a later stage of development (Level 4), children will be able to carry out a fair test in which they are able to identify one variable to be measured (continuous, dependent variable) and one variable to be changed (non-continuous, independent variable). This might arise from an investigation where the question posed is whether the size of a particular type of ball affects the height of its bounce. Some children might predict that 'the bigger the ball the more it will bounce', while others may predict that the 'smaller the ball the more it will bounce'. It should be noted that at this stage both variables should not be continuous or that two independent variables are introduced, for example, weight and size.

Helping children to plan investigations

In our experience, and that of our student teachers and teachers on in-service courses, children have difficulties in planning investigations, at least in terms of which we are made aware. While written plans may lack detail and may be difficult to understand, children are able to explain more clearly by verbal communication and can show how to carry out a test in practice even better still. In view of this we believe that children need a framework in which to plan their investigations which gives them a clear idea of what they are going to do. We have found that the format below (the Science Investigation Planning Form, see photocopiable page 180) is useful in helping children to consider what they are trying to find out, to make predictions, to identify the variables involved, the equipment they require and to measure the appropriate factors.

Despite being given a format for planning, which could be used for most or all investigations, children (and adults) find it difficult to plan in the abstract and must be given concrete experience of interacting with the equipment and materials. There will usually be a need to rethink and modify the plan in the light of these experiences. Nevertheless, it is still useful for children to have time to think through their actions on paper, before starting to carry out the investigation in practice.

Competency in planning will come mainly through children actually gaining practice of carrying out planning and by

Science Investigation Planning Form

Ali

Stage in planning

What do I want to find out? (Title of my investigation.)	Do large sponge balls bounce more than small sponge balls?
What I think will happen. (My prediction.)	The large ones will bounce more than the small ones.
Why I think this will happen.	Because there is more sponge bouncing.
What I need to observe, measure or count (Dependent variable).	The height each ball bounces. ~~The number of~~
Equipment needed and units used.	Metre ruler. Measure to the nearest centimetre.

challenging the children on their ideas and fair tests. But a variety of approaches are beneficial in improving the ability to plan, such as the teacher planning investigations and setting up fair tests by question and answer sessions involving the children (see Chapter 2). In this way the children learn by seeing the planning format used directly and successfully. Children could also work with good examples of workcards where good practice of controlling variables is shown and is made explicit and, by discussing the children's plans after they have carried out their own investigations (see Chapter 2).

An activity where variables are manipulated (and measured) at Level 4 is shown on this page.

After consideration of the equipment used in various sports, the children could be asked why balls of different sizes and materials are used. This could lead to an investigation to find out whether the size of a particular type of ball affects its bounce and where the children are asked to construct fair tests and manipulative variables.

3. Does the size of a ball affect its bounce height?

Age range
Key Stage 2.

Group size
Small groups.

What you need
Three balls of different diameter made from the same material; metre ruler with millimetre gradations; stop clock or watch; large sheet of paper; photocopiable page 180. Materials and equipment should be selected by the children.

What to do
The pupils should be encouraged to design an investigation to find out whether the size of a ball affects the height of its bounce, in response to a suggestion from one of the class or the teacher.

Ensure that the children plan their investigation thoroughly with the help of the Science Investigation Planning Form.

As the children plan, design and carry out their investigation, the teacher should check whether they are carrying out a fair test (see below). Children should be asked to describe if and why their test is fair. Ensure that the children record their results in a systematic way and interpret them. Was their prediction correct?

Investigative skills
The construction of a fair test is fundamental to scientific investigation, in order that meaningful results are obtained. A fair test would be achieved by dropping the ball from a fixed height (say, 1m) in a regular manner (held in the fingers and dropped or 'balanced' on the edge of the metre ruler). The children should have selected three balls of the same material/type (e.g. sponge), as the balls themselves are the focus of the investigation. These are the control variables as they are controlled within the investigation.

The size of ball is the independent variable, the variable the investigator chooses to change. If the children have made a prediction such as 'Small balls will bounce best', the teacher should ensure that the fair testing procedure is not compromised by any bias on the part of the investigator, to help verify the hypothesis! The height each sized ball bounces is the dependent variable and will be measured in centimetres (cm) and possibly millimetres (mm).

In this investigation it is relatively easy to design and maintain a fair test as only three or four factors need to be controlled: the height from which the ball is dropped, the manner in which it is dropped, the choice of three balls of the same material and possibly making sure that that balls bounced on the same place on the same surface. Other investigations may be far more complex. For instance, an investigation to find out which washing powder removes grass stains from a white PE kit best would involve a number of control variables such as the amount of washing powder, the extent of the stain, the temperature of the water, the time it was washed for, where and how it was dried, and so on.

Further activity
Would the children like to carry out any further tests, for example the effect of different surfaces on the ability to bounce?

AT1/4a

Appropriate fair tests should be carried out depending on the abilities and experience of the children involved. It is difficult for children to always identify *all* the variables to be controlled, particularly if there are a number of them, and teachers must make judgements about the importance of these omitted variables. They should also be aware that it may be more difficult to identify variables to be controlled than it is to actually control them in an investigation. For instance, in the investigation above, children may drop the balls fairly automatically (in a controlled manner), but may not be able to identify the manner in which they dropped the balls as a variable to be controlled. Suffice it to say that they have carried out a fair test. Conversely, children might identify variables to be controlled, for example the height from which balls are dropped, but might not adhere to this during testing. If so, they have not carried out a fair test and this raises the question as to whether or not they have achieved Level 4b. In this case, Level 3c may be a more appropriate level of achievement.

Size of sample

Another aspect of fair testing not previously mentioned in this chapter is the size of sample to be considered. Taking the example above, one bounce of the large, medium and small sponge balls may not be sufficient to give meaningful results for a number of reasons. For example, one of the balls may have hit a crack in the floor and bounced erratically or the person measuring the bounce might have made an error of judgement. For this reason a larger sample size than one should be considered and implemented. However, while improving the validity of results, and hence the quality of interpretation of results and conclusions, a larger sample size brings about difficulties for teachers and children alike. The choice of say five results for the bounce of each ball leads to a mathematical demand which may be too much for some children. If a calculator is not used to determine averages, the difficulty may be overcome by taking the median result (e.g. out of five samples, the median would be the middle value in size). A further problem with taking multiple samples is the amount of time which this sometimes involves (though it is not so serious a problem in this bouncing balls investigation), with its possible subsequent reduction in motivation. While persistence is a characteristic considered to indicate possible high ability in science, teachers must use their discretion in determining the number of samples to be taken. Ten is often more than sufficient but offers easier averaging; three or five samples is often adequate but children should be aware that the bigger the sample the better, within the restriction of time.

The final stage in competency regarding fair testing, at least as far as the primary school is concerned (Level 5), involves children selecting the range of each of the variables in order to produce meaningful results. An example of an activity illustrating this is shown below.

Following work on forces or on bridges the pupils might investigate the strength of their bridge (how it sags) when different weights (forces) are applied to it.

4. The effect of weight (mass) on a bridge

Age range
Key Stage 2.

What you need
Bridge made by the children, weights (masses), stop-watch or clock, ruler to measure 'sag standard' (see Figure 1 on the next page).

What to do
Encourage the children to think of ways in which they might test their bridge (but not necessarily to destruction) after they have planned and designed it. They might do this by quantifying the amount of sag as weights are added. Get the pupils to identify the independent variable which they are changing systematically (weight or mass), the dependent variable which they are trying to measure (amount of sag) and the control variables which they are trying to keep constant in order to make it a fair test (weights/masses placed in the same position on the bridge each time and the sag measured at the same length of time after weight/ masses are added).

Investigative skills
Children could be encouraged to identify the independent, dependent and control variables. The teacher should check whether the children have successfully identified the appropriate range, numbers and values to be recorded. The range of weights might depend on those available in the classroom, but the teacher should make sure

that if the bridge is very flimsy that small, e.g. 100g weights/masses are added each time. However, if the bridge is sturdy the teacher should check that a reasonable range of weights (masses) is added. If the child thought that her bridge might collapse with 5kg weight added, the children might choose to load the bridge in 0.5kg (11 readings or numbers including 0g) or 1kg (6 readings or numbers and 6 values) gradations. This would then be sufficient to produce a line graph. This experience of the potential strength of their bridge would have been obtained on previous work with similar materials.

Identification of a fair test may be considered in terms of the position of the weights and the time after adding the weights that sag measurements are made.

AT1/4b,5b

In *Science in the National Curriculum* (1991), the example given at Level 5b involves children in selecting the range of temperature to ensure that bread rises. From prior experience the children should be aware that bread rises within a relatively narrow range of temperatures due to the presence of yeast, a living organism which produces carbon dioxide, causing the bread dough to rise. They should therefore be able to identify temperature as the independent variable and choose a range of values between 20°C and 60°C. They might decide that they require 5 readings/numbers at 20°C, 30°C, 40°C, 50°C and 60°C. They would need to identify time as the dependent variable and ensure that measurable changes could be obtained in the time available. Thus, bread dough at 5°C or 10°C would rise very slowly or not at all, indicating that the children had not selected the correct range. It will be appreciated here that, as well as fair testing to a degree of complexity, the children are being asked to consider their testing in conjunction with their scientific knowledge, understanding or theory. In a similar way, at Levels 3–5, children are asked to make predictions and hypotheses based on experience, prior scientific knowledge, understanding or theory. The National Curriculum has

certainly ensured that science knowledge and scientific investigation are integrally linked (see Chapter 3).

Some children in primary and junior schools who might be working towards Level 6, need to consider all aspects of fair testing encountered at Level 5 but in addition need to 'make qualitative or quantitative observations involving fine discrimination'. The example given in the National Curriculum document illustrates a chemical reaction involving acids where children need to time the reaction until there is a 1g loss in weight. While not having the appropriate materials for this particular investigation, primary and junior schools might, more importantly and significantly, not possess measuring instruments which are as accurate as those suggested here. However, all is not lost, because children can take measurements with a considerable level of accuracy using minor divisions or in between divisions, with instruments such as thermometers and forcemeters (newton meters).

In addition, the children must identify the type of variables involved, the key continuous variables and the key control variables. Thus, in an investigation on dissolving sugar, the children could see how long it takes for different sizes of grains of sugar (e.g. fine, granular, cubed) to dissolve at different temperatures. The key to successful investigations and obtaining valid scientific data lies in setting up a fair test where the variables to be controlled, the variable to be measured and the variable to be systematically changed are identified and manipulated.

Figure 1

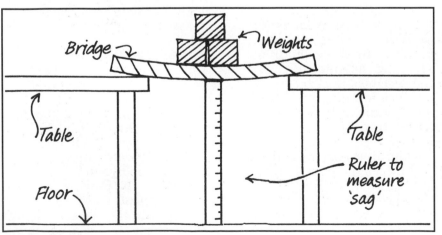

CHAPTER 5

Measuring, selecting equipment and carrying out investigations

Measurement is a way of determining quantities of temperature, time, length, mass, area and volume. It provides information about changes during investigations or helps children compare situations.

Children need to develop the skill of reading and using a variety of measuring instruments in science investigations. They also need to be able to apply measurement within investigations by relating conceptual understanding to skills of using measuring instruments. It is important to take into account the child's stage of development when considering the skills of measurement and choosing equipment. Children need to understand numbers, for example, before they can use rulers or thermometers.

BACKGROUND

As children make progress in carrying out scientific investigations they will recognise the need to use equipment to enable them to quantify their observations. There is a progression from the use of qualitative to quantitative methods in investigations as children move from Key Stage 1 to Key Stage 2. They will need to use measures to say how much or how long. This will at first be through using non-standard units such as hand spans to measure lengths or toy bricks to measure distance or height. Soon they will realise that these units must be the same, for example, the same handspan must be used to compare widths or lengths. At this stage, the children can be introduced to simple standard measures such as rulers which are marked with the standard units but with no minor divisions on them. Measuring instruments will become more precise with minor divisions on them as the complexity of the investigation develops.

During investigations the children will acquire the skill of choosing appropriate equipment to enhance their observations. They will want to measure time so will select a stop-clock or stop-watch. If they need to measure temperature they will select a thermometer as the appropriate measuring instrument.

Children will need help at first in making decisions as to *when* they should make measurements, *what* they should measure and *how* they should measure (see Figure 1). If the children are to investigate and measure the similarities and differences between themselves (KS2 AT2 Pos(ii)) they must decide *what* measurements they are going to make (pulse rate, height and so on), *when* they will make these measurements, and *how* they are going to make them (AT1 PoS). They need to consider what instruments they will use, for example, stop-watch, tape measure, and what units they will measure in, for example, minutes or seconds, metres or centimetres. Other decisions they will need to make are how accurate these measurements need to be and how many times they should check or repeat the measurements.

Children should be given opportunities to learn how to use a thermometer or to make accurate measurements with a ruler. They will come to understand that they should choose the appropriate unit to measure a particular quantity, for example, they would not use a 15cm ruler to measure the distance across the playground (AT1/3b).

It is important to incorporate into the discussion and planning of all investigations a time which specifically includes decisions concerning what measurements will need to be made and what equipment is to be used for making those measurements.

As children start to use more complex measuring instruments they should be aware of the importance of

Figure 1

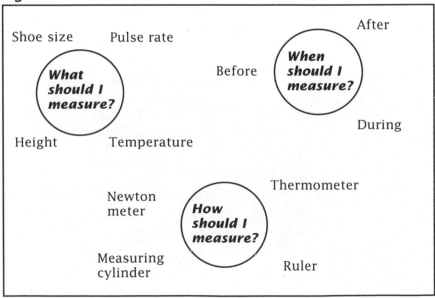

accuracy. Encourage them to consider the degree of accuracy which is required. How accurate do they need to be in a particular situation? Measurements will become more precise as the level of complexity of the investigation increases. It is important for the children to be able to consider which is the appropriate item of equipment to use in order to achieve a higher degree of accuracy.

Accuracy can also be improved by repeating measurements and examining consistency of readings. At Level 5, children are required to choose a range of variables to produce meaningful results. It would be important, therefore, in some situations for the children to select a range of appropriate measurements, for example, a range of temperature readings if they are testing the effect of temperature change on a biological process such as the rate at which bread dough rises.

There are, therefore, a number of stages which children will go through in developing measuring skills:
1. Children will need first to be able to make simple observations.
2. Children should recognise the need to quantify their observations in some way. This may be through comparisons or by sequencing.
3. Non-standard units should be introduced.
4. Standard units should be introduced.

5. Children should gain practice in using simple measuring instruments to enhance observations.
6. Children should make estimations of measurements before choosing the appropriate instrument for their investigation.
7. Children should decide *when*, *what* and *how* they are going to measure.
8. Children should select the appropriate measuring instruments for their investigation.
9. The degree of accuracy of measurement has to be selected and the appropriate instrument needed to give this required degree of accuracy should be used.

Measurement skills

These involve the correct use of measuring instruments and reading of the scales:
• ruler – read metres, centimetres or millimetres as appropriate. The unit will be

determined by the scale of the object being measured.
• thermometer – allow three minutes for it to display the correct reading and then read to the nearest two degrees Celsius.
• measuring cylinder – place on a flat surface and read at eye level with the lowest part of the curve (meniscus). It is important to use an appropriate sized measuring cylinder for the investigation.
• stop-clock or stop-watch – set the timer to zero and then read minutes or seconds as appropriate.
• balance or weighing scales – read the mass in grams or kilograms as appropriate.

Always write down the units once the reading has been made.

The following two activities can be used to help children observe closely and quantify by measuring using appropriate instruments (AT1/3b).

SAMPLE ACTIVITIES

1. Investigating temperature

Age range
Five to eleven.

Group size
Pairs or small groups.

What you need
A number of spirit thermometers with a range of −10 to 110°C, a variety of other spirit thermometers with different ranges, paper, pencils, hot and cold water from the taps, a beaker containing ice cubes.

What to do
Discuss changes in temperature in summer and winter weather and the importance of keeping food cool in the fridge or freezer. Discuss body temperature and how temperature is raised during illness when we have a fever.

Ask the children how we measure temperature and how we can find out the temperature in different places, for example, the classroom, in a sunny place, in a cool place, near a radiator, in the fridge, out of doors, in the shade.

The children can examine different thermometers. How are they different? How are they the same? Which would be appropriate for measuring the classroom temperature? What unit do we use to measure temperature?

They can then carry out an investigation to compare two thermometers. Do they give the same readings in water from hot and cold taps and in a beaker containing ice cubes? What if one of the thermometers is in an upright position and one is lying down? How long should the children keep the thermometer in position before taking a reading? Where exactly should the thermometer be when they take the reading?

Investigative skills
The children are developing the skill of selecting an appropriate instrument for measuring temperature. They have considered when they should take the temperature reading and they have used a thermometer to measure the temperatures. Skill in reading the instrument is being developed. Children are drawing comparisons between two instruments.

Content
Temperature is a measure of how hot or cold it is and is now measured using the Celsius scale. These record the temperature of melting ice at 0°C and boiling water at 100°C. The thermometer should be placed in position and three minutes allowed for it to display the correct reading before the temperature is taken.

Safety
Always use a spirit thermometer and not a mercury thermometer. Mercury is poisonous and a potential hazard if the thermometer breaks.

Handle thermometers with care as they are made of glass.

AT1/3b PoS; AT4/2b PoS(ii)

2. Investigating volume

Age range
Eight to eleven.

Group size
Pairs or small groups.

What you need
A range of measuring cylinders of different capacities, stones or appropriate everyday objects of different sizes, string, measuring jugs of different sizes, transparent beakers.

What to do
This investigation enables the children to choose appropriate sized measuring cylinders for measuring volume for a particular purpose. Discuss with the children the fact that when an object is put into water the level of the water rises. Compare this with getting into the bath and watching the water level rise. The water is being pushed aside or displaced. This notion of displacement can be used to measure the volume of objects.

The children should investigate the volume of different sized objects. They can attach string to the objects and lower them slowly into measuring cylinders containing known quantities of water. As the objects go into the water the level of the water rises. If the level goes up by 15cm this must be the space taken by the object. They should make sure their eye is level with the bottom of the water curve when they read the volume of water in the measuring cylinder.

Alternatively, a beaker could be filled to the brim with water. As an object is lowered into the beaker some of the water will overflow. The children should use an appropriately sized measuring jug to fill up the beaker to the top again. The amount of water used is equal to the volume of the object.

Investigative skills
The children are developing the skill of selecting and using appropriate measuring equipment to measure volume.

Content
Archimedes discovered that the upward push on an object in a liquid (the upthrust) is equal to the weight of the liquid displaced. Objects float when the upthrust on them is strong enough to balance their weight. Whether an object floats or not depends on its density and shape. A ship is shaped so that it displaces a lot of water.

AT1/3b PoS

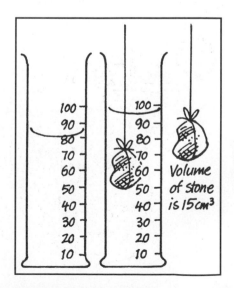

Volume of stone is 15cm³

CHAPTER 6

Recording and communicating results

It is important for children to communicate their thoughts and ideas at all stages of their scientific activities and at all levels of their development. 'They should have the opportunity to express their findings and ideas to other children orally and through drawings, charts, models, actions and writing' (Science in the National Curriculum 1991).

Children should develop an understanding of the purposes of recording results and recognise that there are different methods of recording which are appropriate for different types of results.

BACKGROUND

Purposes of recording

Children do not need to record everything they do within their scientific investigations but it is important that they understand *when* and *why* they record. If they record their work they will think about their ideas in more depth and begin to take responsibility for their learning. They will want to share their ideas with others and compare their findings. Recording and communicating are part of the learning process.

Recording can be an aid to observation. The child is able to consolidate her ideas through oral communication and through drawings and diagrams.

Recording can also help in planning and ordering of ideas. It helps children sequence their thoughts in a logical way. It is often essential to the progress of the investigation that children note down their results, for example, measuring temperatures or times to be represented later on a bar chart or line graph.

Another purpose of recording is to recall events which have taken place throughout the investigation. Again, this encourages logical thinking and often makes interpretation of results easier.

Skills of communication are developed progressively and children learn that they can express their ideas, observations and results in a variety of ways. They learn how to list and record data systematically and how to represent their results in a graphical form.

Children are able gradually to select the most appropriate ways of recording and representing their data and are able to become more selective in what they record. At a higher level, it is helpful for children to think about how they are going to record their results before they start to collect them. This will help them to decide in more open investigations what kind of observations and measurements to write down. It also helps children to record them more efficiently and accurately.

Recording is also helpful when the time comes for children to interpret their results and recognise patterns. It is a good starting point for discussion with the teacher and the rest of the class.

From a practical point of view, recording can provide evidence for assessment purposes. The teacher will have a permanent record of

the children's work and understanding of scientific concepts, and vital clues to the children's thinking. Progress in skill development is also observed and teachers are provided with useful evidence for assessing children on aspects of practical activities.

Progression in recording skills

Recording and communicating skills increase their complexity as the children gain more experience carrying out scientific investigations. It is often through the process of recording and communicating observations and results that children come to reflect upon their ideas and order them to make sense of their investigation. It is essential that the type of recording is matched to the level of development of the child and to the type of scientific activity undertaken.

Communication and recording at the very early stages (Level 1) should be achieved through discussion with other children and the teacher. It is helpful if these discussions are ongoing throughout the investigation rather than just at the end of the activity. It is through such discussions with others that

children are able to sort out and question their ideas and share them with their peers. Class or group discussion work led by the teacher can be very valuable. The teacher can ask a series of open-ended questions helping the children to think for themselves.

Children should then be encouraged to represent their data in a written form (Levels 2/3). At first this may be through drawings and charts but this will lead to recording findings in simple tables or bar charts (Levels 3/4). Ordering and sequencing skills are important skills to be developed and children must be taught how to draw such tables and bar charts. Drawing line graphs and presenting more formal reports are appropriate for children at Levels 4/5.

Children should be encouraged to make notes during their scientific activities. Jotting down their plans, ideas, observations and results is one of the best ways of keeping a record. This will help during formal reporting as it encourages children to

start thinking in a logical way so that they can explain to others what they have done. Opportunities for others to raise questions will also be provided during formal reporting.

Children should learn and practise the skills of recording data in a systematic way, representing it in the form of frequency tables, bar charts and line graphs.

Frequency tables, block graphs, bar charts and line graphs

There are two types of frequency tables:
• a simple frequency table;
• a grouped frequency table.
A good example of how information can be organised into a frequency table is shown for results of a shoe-size survey in a class of 30 children. The results might be:
3, 3, 5, 6, 1, 6, 4, 5, 4, 3, 2, 3, 3, 4, 5, 2, 3, 3, 5, 4, 7, 2, 3, 2, 4, 7, 4, 3, 5, 8.

These results can then be incorporated into a frequency table:

Shoe size	Number of children
1	1
2	4
3	9
4	6
5	5
6	2
7	2
8	1

A grouped frequency table combines separate values into groups which are of equal size. An example is shown below. Data from a class survey of children's heights is grouped into equal bands. The result (height in centimetres) for a class of 24 children could be:

145, 132, 164, 117, 136, 127, 171, 115, 138, 146, 134, 141, 158, 129, 130, 142, 138, 154, 139, 145, 163, 122, 137, 151.

A grouped frequency table can then be drawn which groups the heights into bands. The number of heights in each group is found by adding up the relevant results.

Height (cm)	Number of children
110–119	2
120–129	3
130–139	8
140–149	5
150–159	3
160–169	2
170–179	1

Information from both types of frequency tables can be represented in graphical form. It is often easier to see patterns in results by drawing a graph. The type of graph to be drawn depends on the type of data collected.

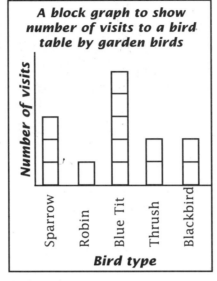

Figure 1

Block graphs can be used to represent a simple set of data such as a record of the number and type of birds which might visit a bird table in the school grounds (see Figure 1). The results might be:

Bird type	Number of visits
Sparrow	3
Robin	1
Blue Tit	5
Thrush	2
Blackbird	2

Bar charts can be constructed to represent data, for example, a survey of pets in the class or variation in eye colour or tongue-rolling ability (see Figure 2).

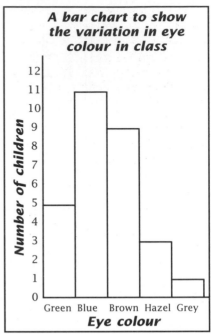

Figure 2

A line graph is drawn for a set of single results such as variation of temperature in a day or distance covered by a car in a given time. It is important to remember when interpreting the graph that the intermediate values on a line graph may not have a meaning (see Figure 3).

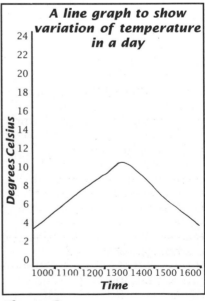

Figure 3

Report writing involves the children in placing events in a logical order and expressing their ideas clearly. Children may find it helpful to follow a simple written format such as:
• what I used
• what I did
• what I saw
• what I found out
or they could devise a format of their own through discussion with the teacher. It is helpful to record parts of the activity as it is ongoing. Encourage the children to read through their report to a friend after they have written it. They may wish to add to it when ideas have been shared.

Children should start to use scientific terms when recording and communicating. Encourage the use of such terms in verbal discussions and in written work. It is vital, however, that they understand the meaning of the words in order for learning and communication to be effective. Words such as melting, freezing, solid, liquid, gas, dissolve, acid, alkali are just some examples of vocabulary which children should be encouraged to use and feel confident about.

Table 1 shows the progression of recording skills from simple to more complex.

Different ways of recording

These are some possible methods of recording and communicating results.
1. Verbal recording
• discussion in pairs;
• group discussion;
• group discussion led by the teacher;
• formal reporting – back to a group or the whole class;
• audio tape played to group or whole class;
• recording through drama, poetry or stories.
2. Pictorial representation
• painting, e.g. to record the effects of colour mixing;

Table 1

Methods of communicating and recording results		
	Level	Example of appropriate activity
Talking	1	Talking about favourite foods and food eaten at breakfast, dinner and evening meal.
Drawings	1/2	Drawing a flowering plant to identify the main external parts.
Charts	2/3	Classifying everyday materials into different types using properties such as rough and smooth.
Pictograms	3	Recording weather conditions over a period of time. Children devise their own weather symbols and draw a pictogram.
Frequency tables	3/4	Counting mini-beasts in a sample area in the school playground.
Tables	3/4	Constructing a simple two-column table which identifies substances which dissolve and those which do not dissolve.
Block graphs and bar charts	2/3/4	Carrying out a bird survey – numbers of different types of birds which visit the bird table in the playground over a period of one or two weeks.
Line graphs	4/5	Recording the height of plants over a period of time.
Formal report	4/5	Reporting on an investigation which considers the factors that affect the rate at which bread dough rises.

- a picture to show the solution to a problem;
- diagrams – clearly labelled;
- flow diagrams – to show the order of events;
- charts – results are recorded in a systematic organised way;
- graphs – block graph, pictogram, histogram, line graph;
- pie-charts – this is a higher level skill;
- 3-D recording – collections of leaves, bark rubbings, models.

3. Written work
- factual writing – includes note-taking;
- creative writing;
- comprehension – to reinforce ideas – cloze procedure;
- worksheets.

4. Using audio-visual equipment
- cameras;
- tape recorders;
- video recorders.

5. Computers
- information retrieval;
- graphics;
- word processing.

Presenting data

The emphasis should be on children generating, collecting and using their own data. There are a number of advantages to this as identified by Taylor and Swatton (1991).

1. Children 'own' the data and thus its collection and content are familiar to them.

2. The children can compare their results and methods of collecting the information with other children or groups.

3. Comparing and evaluating their own results should encourage the children to look at errors and reflect on their own measurement strategies.

4. It helps develop their understanding of the purposes of recording and presenting their results.

5. It provides teachers with useful evidence for assessment.

This does not mean, however, that children should not be encouraged to use data which have not been generated by themselves. For example, data can be presented which relate to wider contexts where it would be difficult to carry out suitable classroom investigations.

Data presented in graphical form

Assessment of Performance Unit (APU) findings provide an indication of what we can expect from children in relation to data presented in graphical form.

At Level 3 children should be able to add data (numerical, pictorial or verbal) to a table which is drawn for them or add data involving whole numbers to a simple bar chart where axes and scales are already drawn and labelled. They should be able to read information from simple bar charts.

At Level 4 children should be able to construct and label simple two-column tables and enter data correctly or be able to draw from scratch simple bar charts or line graphs using data involving whole numbers.

At Level 5 children should be able to describe and interpret patterns in simple data presented in a table, bar chart or line graph which may or may not be self-generated.

There is a link between making measurements and collecting data and representing the data in graphical form. Children may be able to see more easily the need for taking a series of measurements over a range or repeating measurements for accuracy if they practise the skill of constructing and interpreting graphs of their own results. Thinking about the way they are going to present their results may influence their planning concerning what measurements they are going to make. On the opposite page is an example of an activity showing the use of a frequency table and bar chart to record results.

1. Investigating shoe size – frequency table and bar chart

Age range
Eight to eleven.

Group size
Individuals, whole class.

What you need
Paper, pencils and square paper.

What to do
Discuss with the children similarities and differences between individuals (see Chapter 12, Ourselves) – height, eye colour and so on. Ask the children to look at their feet – what size are their shoes? Are they bigger than their friends' shoes? Is there a relationship between the height of the child and shoe size?

Discuss with the children how they might carry out an investigation to see if there is such a relationship. They may hypothesise that the taller the child the larger the feet and thus the bigger the shoe size.

The children can carry out a survey collecting data on shoe sizes in the class. Encourage them to think about the best way to collect and record their data. Show them how to organise their information in a frequency table. This will give an idea of the variation of shoe sizes in the class and can be used to draw a bar chart. They

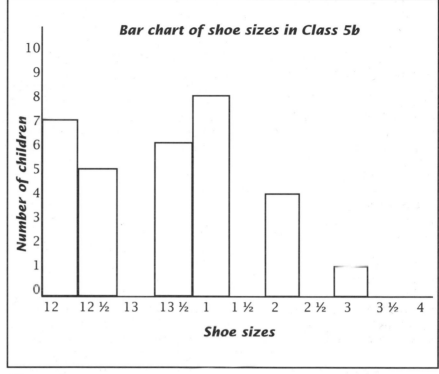

Figure 1

should find the smallest and largest shoe sizes and use these for the first and last readings in the 'shoe sizes' column of their frequency table. The axes and scales on the bar chart could be already drawn and labelled as shown in Figure 1.

Encourage the children to interpret the data and identify differences in shoe size and the range of foot size in the class.

Investigative skills
The children have systematically listed and recorded their data in a frequency table. They have

represented their data by drawing a bar chart. This activity could be attempted at two levels – Level 3 where the children add data to a pre-drawn table and to a bar chart where axes and scales are already drawn, or Level 4 where the children construct their own frequency table and bar chart from scratch.

Content
The children have investigated differences between themselves. There will be a range of shoe sizes in the class.

AT1 PoS; AT2 PoS(ii)

CHAPTER 7

Interpreting results, evaluating evidence and drawing conclusions

An important part of the investigative process for children is the interpretation of results and the seeking and establishment of patterns or relationships derived from data. There is a distinct progression from simple to more complex through the levels of attainment in the development of all the investigative skills: interpretation, pattern seeking and drawing conclusions. There is a shift in the type of data from qualitative to quantitative. If the child has a set of observations arising from an investigation, she must look at these to see what they mean. Following on from this stage is considering whether the interpretation of the observations supports the original hypothesis. This is called drawing a conclusion.

The children will interpret their findings initially by association of one factor with another. This can be encouraged by presenting them with appropriate investigations such as testing whether objects will float or sink. They should then make interpretations related to their results and use their observations to support conclusions. They can then compare what they have observed with what they expected (Level 2). An activity which encourages the development of this skill is shown on the next page.

Line graph

Will float

Will not float

DAY	WEATHER	TEMP.
Mon	Sunny	20°
Tues	Cloudy	15°
Wed	Wet	11°
Thurs	Sunny	18°
Fri	Windy	9°

To make the bulb light we needed to make a complete circuit

SAMPLE ACTIVITIES

1. Floating and sinking

Age range
Key Stage 1.

Group size
Small groups.

What you need
A large washing-up bowl, a collection of everyday objects, for example, a pencil, a stone, a Lego brick, a coin, a paper-clip, a cork.

What to do
Fill the washing-up bowl with water. Discuss with the children which objects they think will float and which will sink. They will now carry out an investigation to see which objects float and which sink. They can work in small groups and choose some of the objects to test. Encourage the children to predict before they put it in the water whether the object will float or sink. How are they going to record their results? A chart could be made which shows two sets of objects – those which float and those which sink. Ask the children to think carefully about their results. How are the floating objects similar? Why do they think these objects have floated?

Investigative skills
At this early stage, children will probably say that the light objects floated and the heavy objects sank. They have interpreted their findings by associating lightness of the object with its capability to float. They have used their observations to support conclusions: 'Heavy objects sink, light objects float'. They have related these observations to their predictions.

Content
Whether or not an object floats depends upon its density and its shape. If the object is denser than the fluid it will sink. Whenever an object is lowered into a fluid and displaces some of the fluid, there is an upthrust caused by the pressure of the surrounding fluid. The upthrust is equal to the weight of the fluid displaced. For a floating object, the upthrust equals the weight of the object. A ship is shaped so that it displaces a lot of water and there is a large upthrust as a result.

AT1/2c PoS; AT4 PoS(iii)

Level 3
The children will then progress in their interpretation skills by being able to interpret their observations in a more general way. When investigating the stretching of a spring, for example, it is important to encourage them to look for a general trend (Level 3). They should be able to distinguish between a description of what they observed and a simple explanation of how and why it happened. This can be shown in the next activity.

2. Stretching a spring

Age range
Key Stage 2.

Group size
Small groups.

What you need
A steel spring, weights – 50g, 100g, 200g, 300, 400g – paper, pencils.

What to do
A simple activity can be carried out to investigate the behaviour of a spring. What happens when we try to stretch it? The increase in length of the spring is called its extension. Ask the children to investigate how a spring is stretched. They can suspend a spring from a hook, measure its length, then put weights of increasing mass on the end of the spring and measure the new lengths. What happens to the spring when the weights are removed? Does it return to its original length?

The length of the spring should be measured each time a heavier weight is put on to it. Ask the children to predict what will happen as heavier loads are put on to the spring. They can then record their results in a table like the one below. Encourage the children to look for a pattern in their results. What happens as the load is increased?

Investigative skills
The children should be able to see that as the loads get heavier the spring extends more. Encourage them to make a generalisation that the greater the load the longer the spring. The spring always returns to its original length when the loads are removed from it. The children will have interpreted their observations in terms of a generalised statement. They have observed that as heavier weights are added, the longer the spring gets. They should have explained that this is because the spring stretches. If a line graph of the extension of the spring against the mass of the load was to be drawn, a straight line would result. There is a point at which, if heavier and heavier loads were put on the spring, it would not return to its original length and would eventually break.

Content
A spring obeys Hooke's Law – the extension is directly proportional to the load until the spring reaches its elastic limit. This means that at this point when the load is removed from the spring, it no longer returns to its original shape and length.

A simple way of measuring a force is to use it to stretch a spring. A spring with a scale attached to it is called a newton meter and this is used to measure forces. Forces are measured in newtons. Weight is a force and can be measured with a newton meter. A mass of one kilogram weighs about 10 newtons.

AT1/3d PoS; AT4/3c PoS(iii)

Mass of Load (g)	Length of spring (cm)
No load	
50	
100	
200	
300	
400	

Level 4

At Level 4 children should be able to draw conclusions which link patterns in observations or results to the original question, prediction or idea.

An example of such an investigation which would enable children to develop this level of skill would be if they were asked the best way to slow down the melting of an ice cube.

The children might suggest wrapping ice cubes in insulating material and may predict that thicker materials would be more effective than thinner ones in slowing down melting. *(AT1/4a)* They could test this out by using a variety of scrap materials as insulators and timing how long the ice cubes wrapped in the different materials take to melt. They should discuss how to set up a fair test and recognise that their conclusions may not be valid unless a fair test has been carried out. *(AT1/3c)* Remind them to consider the variables involved. They could use the following questions to help them design a fair test:
• What will change?
• What will stay the same?
• What are we trying to measure and what instrument will we use to measure it? *(AT1/4b)*

Encourage discussion on the most appropriate way to record the results. The children will need to record both the starting time and the finishing time, that is, the time the ice cubes are removed from the freezer and the time by which the ice cubes have turned to water completely.

The children could use their observations and results (the ice cube wrapped in the thick material took twelve minutes to melt, but the ice cube wrapped in the thinnest material took only three minutes to melt) to conclude that the thickest insulating material is the most effective in slowing down the melting process. *(AT1/4c)*

NB For this investigation the children could either compare different insulating materials wrapped round the ice cubes the same number of times, *or* the same insulating material wrapped round the ice cubes an increasing number of times, that is, varying numbers of layers of the same material.

Level 5

At Level 5, children should be encouraged to evaluate the validity of their conclusions and consider different explanations of their results.

The children could carry out an investigation to find out which conditions woodlice prefer. They might wish to investigate whether they prefer a dark habitat to a light habitat. They could set up a choice chamber (a dish divided into two halves with access from one half of the dish into the other), put a layer of soil in the bottom of it, and place a specified number of woodlice in the dish at the halfway point. If the children then cover one half of the dish so that it is in the dark, and leave the other half of the dish open to the light, they could observe where the woodlice are after a period of a few days.

The children should consider different explanations for the movement of the woodlice to the dark part of the chamber. One explanation could be that the woodlice prefer dark conditions. Another explanation could be that the woodlice prefer the dark chamber because it is damp. In this part of the chamber the moisture will have been retained in the soil, whereas the moisture will have evaporated from the soil which is in the uncovered light part of the chamber. *(AT1/5c)*

Drawing a conclusion

Children should attempt to explain their results from their investigations, i.e. draw a conclusion. There are several stages involved in drawing a conclusion. The children should:
• obtain a set of results and

check or compare these results with other children's.
• organise the results into a chart, graph, drawing or other form so that the information is easy to understand.
• look for relationships or patterns in the results. There may not be an exact relationship but it still may be possible to see some overall trends. Look for patterns across a number of sets of results, not just one group's
• examine other information which may be relevant – are the results similar to any that have been obtained from another investigation? Try and link patterns in observations or results to the original hypothesis or prediction.
• if possible, use scientific knowledge to help explain what has been observed. Produce written statements of patterns or relationships which have come from a number of sources.
• try and build up links with

other investigations that have been carried out in the past. Are there any common patterns resulting from these?
• evaluate conclusions which have been drawn by considering other possible explanations for what has occurred.
• once a conclusion has been drawn it may be appropriate to make a new hypothesis or suggest a new idea and begin another investigation.

Helping children make interpretations

In order to help children develop the skills of interpretation there are a number of simple strategies that can be used.
1. Encourage the children to consider simple connections within their results, for

Why do you think the woodlice preferred the dark side of the tray?

example, at early stages children might say 'Light objects float.'

2. Encourage the children to represent data in different forms as appropriate, for example, when should children draw a bar graph, why are graphs helpful? Discuss with the children how useful graphs are at clearly showing patterns in results and how useful they are in representing information clearly.

3. Allow the children time to discuss their results in groups and also with the whole class.

4. Present children with problems and data which they have not generated themselves and give them the opportunity to interpret the results and look for patterns in the data.

5. Ask questions such as:
• What do you notice about ....?
• What is the same ....?

• Why do you think that .... happened?
• What do you think would happen if..........?
• Is there any quantity which increases while another decreases?
• How does this factor depend upon another?
• What changes do you notice in the bar chart?
• Is there a link between......?
• Does this happen every time?

Children then need to be taken a stage further in their thinking and evaluate critically what they have done. Encourage them to reflect on the way they have carried out the investigation and on the results they have obtained. Were their results what they

expected? Have they carried out a fair test? Do they need to repeat the test in order to check results, improve accuracy or examine another aspect of the investigation? Have they compared their results with those of other groups and is there a pattern emerging? Has the investigation raised further questions which they would like to investigate?

It is important for teachers to provide opportunities for children to carry out a range of investigations which will help them to develop these skills of interpreting and drawing conclusions and of explaining patterns and relationships in their environment.

CHAPTER 8

Water

Water is essential to life. It plays a vital part in most of our everyday activities: drinking, cooking and washing. Through carrying out investigations related to water, children will develop their knowledge and understanding of the physical, chemical and biological aspects of the world in which they live.

Children will be aware that in some parts of the world there are droughts, in contrast to other areas where devastating floods occur. We need to use our water resources wisely and understand how they can be put at risk. Investigations relating to water will provide many opportunities for children to extend their knowledge and understanding.

Young children could begin their investigations with some exploration of the concepts of floating and sinking. This can be extended into other activities relating to evaporation and filtration. Data collection skills will be developed by carrying out surveys to see how much water is used in a day. The theme of water allows such investigations as the use of red cabbage water for determining whether everyday substances are acid, alkaline or neutral, and the importance of oxygen and water in the rusting process. The melting of ice cubes is the focus for the whole investigation on water. A topic on water is centred upon the child's familiar environment and lends itself to cross-curricular activities.

BACKGROUND

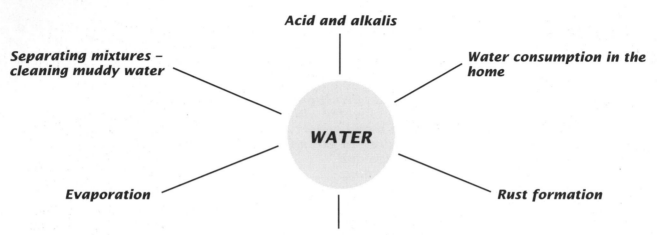

Acid and alkalis

Separating mixtures –
cleaning muddy water

Water consumption in the
home

WATER

Evaporation

Rust formation

Solutions and solubility

Activity	AT1	Statement of attainment
1. Floating shapes	2a 2b 3a 3c	– Question – Observe – Predict – Carry out a fair test
2. Separating mixtures – cleaning muddy water	3a 3d	– Question – Predict – Explain
3. Salty investigations	3a 4a	– Question – Predict
4. Acid or alkali?	4a 4b 4c	– Question – Predict – Carry out a fair test – Measure quantities – Draw conclusions
5. Investigating rust	5a 5c	– Hypothesise – Suggest explanations
6. How much do I use in a day?	PoS	– Collect data – Record – Bar charts/graphs
7. Whole investigation – ice cubes melting	Level 2	

ACTIVITIES

1. Floating shapes

Age range
Key Stage 1 and 2.

Group size
Small groups.

What you need
Large plastic bowl, water, Plasticine, aluminium foil, paper, pencils.

What to do
The children will have done some preliminary investigations to see which objects float in water and which sink. They will have sorted their objects into 'floaters' and 'sinkers' and discussed what all the 'floaters' have in common.

The children should start off by experimenting with a small ball of Plasticine or piece of aluminium foil to see whether these float or sink in a bowl of water. Pose the questions, 'Can you make the Plasticine float', and 'Which shapes float best?'

They will need help in identifying variables such as 'amount of Plasticine used' or 'size of aluminium foil'. How can they make their test fair? They should use the same piece of Plasticine (or other pieces of the same amount) or the same piece of foil. They will need to mould the Plasticine into different shapes and see if they float. Each member of the group should take a turn, testing out a different shape. What do they think will happen if they use twice as much Plasticine or foil? Will the same shapes float or sink then?

The children could then draw pictures of the shapes which floated and the shapes which sank.

Investigative skills
The children have asked the question 'Which shape will float best?' They have made related observations and realised that they should make their test fair.

Content
The shape and density of an object affects whether it will float or sink in water. The amount of water 'pushed aside' or *displaced* by the shape is important. A large ship displaces a lot of water. The water pushed aside exerts an upward push called the *upthrust*. Objects float when the upthrust on them balances their weight. A solid ball of Plasticine will sink but one made into a boat shape should float. At Key Stage 1, children should be aware that a force in the water allows objects to float.

**AT1/2a,2b,3a,3c;
AT4 PoS(iii)**

2. Separating mixtures – cleaning muddy water

P.O.S

Age range
Key Stage 2.

Group size
Small groups.

What you need
Sand, gravel, filter funnel, large jam jar, muddy water (soil and water mixed).

What to do
This activity can be introduced by discussing the problem of how muddy or dirty water from rivers is purified and cleaned at the water treatment works so that it is fit to drink.

Discuss how important it is that the water we drink is cleaned before it is piped to our homes. It is vital to mention that although water may look clean, it may still contain harmful bacteria and chemicals which must also be removed before water is fit to drink.

Tell the children about the water purification process which takes place at the water treatment works (it may be possible to arrange a visit to a plant to see the process). One of the first processes which takes place at the works is the filtering of the water through sand and gravel filter beds to clean it.

Can the children clean muddy water by using this filtration process? They could experiment by placing sand and gravel in layers in a filter funnel and pouring muddy water (soil and water) through the funnel to collect in a jam jar. They could try using very muddy water and slightly muddy water. They could vary the number of layers of sand and gravel to see which is more effective at cleaning the water. How long does the water take to drop through into the jar? Is the water that comes through perfectly clean or do they need to put more layers of sand and gravel in the funnel to achieve clarity?

What happens if the children put their water through the filter a second time? Alternatively, the children could try putting other substances in the filter funnel such as cotton wool or filter paper to see how effective they are at cleaning the water.

After they have carried out their tests they could share their ideas with the class by making posters to display.

Investigative skills
The children have suggested questions, ideas and predictions based on everyday experience (water piped to our home is cleaned so that it is fit to use) and they have tested out these ideas. They have made observations and suggested explanations for these observations.

Content
Filtration is the process of separating an insoluble solid from a liquid. Water is purified at a water treatment works. The water is first filtered through sand and gravel filter beds to remove organic and inorganic debris. The layers of sand and gravel become finer toward the bottom of the beds. The water leaving the filter beds undergoes other treatments. More dirt is removed by a process called sedimentation. Then chlorine is added to the water to remove harmful bacteria.

AT1/3a,3d; AT3/5a PoS(i)

3. Salty investigations

Age range
Key Stage 2.

Group size
Small groups.

What you need
Table salt, water, teaspoons, transparent beakers, graduated cylinders, drinking straws, Blu-tack, permanent waterproof felt-tip pens, hand lenses, saucers or shallow dishes.

What to do
Salt is a chemical substance with which the children will be

very familiar. This activity sets out to explore some of the properties of salt (such as solubility) through some simple investigations.

Discuss with the children how they might carry out an investigation to find out more about salt.

They should be encouraged to pose questions based on prior knowledge. This could be based on observations they have made in the kitchen when salt is added to cooking water and the salt disappears. Will the salt dissolve in water? How much salt will dissolve in water if we keep on adding it to the water? What is the effect of warming the water?

Other questions worth considering might include the following.
• How can we separate the salt from water once we have added it to the water?
• Do objects float more easily in salt water?

The children should be encouraged to predict the answers to these questions before carrying out their investigations. If the children work in groups, each group could carry out a different investigation.

A simple float can be designed from a drinking straw weighted with Blu-tack and marked at regular intervals with a waterproof felt-tip pen. The children could see whether the straw floats more easily in salty water than in ordinary tap water.

Another investigation which could be carried out is testing the solubility of salt in water. Teaspoons of salt could be added to a measured quantity of water. The children could investigate whether more salt will dissolve in warm water than in cold. Is there a point

reached when no more salt will dissolve? Introduce words such as *solution*, *solute* and *solvent*.

The children could design an experiment to find out if they can recover the salt from the water after it has dissolved. If some of the salt solution is placed in a saucer or shallow dish and the dish placed on top of a warm radiator or in the sunshine on a windowsill for a few days, the water will evaporate and salt crystals will remain. The term 'evaporation' can be introduced at this point. The children could then investigate whether it is possible to speed up or slow down the evaporation process.

Investigative skills
The children have asked questions and made predictions based on everyday experience or knowledge. They have then carried out investigations to test out their predictions.

Content
The chemical name for salt is sodium chloride. In some countries, solid salt is obtained by the evaporation of sea water. In Britain, there are underground salt deposits.

When salt is added to water, the salt dissolves and a salt solution is formed. The salt (solid) is called the solute and the water is called the solvent. When a substance dissolves in a liquid it is said to be soluble.

If salt is dissolved in water at room temperature, a point is reached when no more will dissolve. This solution is known as a saturated solution. If the water is warmed, more salt will dissolve before the solution becomes saturated. The salt dissolved in water can be recovered by evaporation. The water is lost into the air, leaving the salt.

AT1/3a,4a; AT3/5a PoS(i)

4. Acid or alkali?

Age range
Key Stage 2.

Group size
Small groups.

What you need
Small red cabbage, chopping board, test tubes or yoghurt pots, warm water in a container, a kitchen knife, dropping pipettes, lemon juice, vinegar, bicarbonate of soda, tea, coffee, orange juice, milk, washing-up liquid, and other everyday substances, cold water to make solutions, graduated cylinders.

What to do

This activity can be introduced by a discussion on acids and alkalis and the fact that chemists use special dyes called indicators to determine whether a substance is an acid or an alkali. It is also possible to use natural indicators such as red cabbage water.

An adult should cut up the red cabbage into small pieces and place it in the warm water. Show the children how it stains the hands and may stain clothes and the chopping board. Put the cabbage pieces into the warm water and leave them for a few minutes. The juice from the cabbage will colour the water purple. Let the water cool. This natural dye is now ready to use for the investigation. (Vegetable skins such as beetroot and onion are also suitable for making indicators.)

The children should then plan their investigation so that they will find out which of the everyday substances are acids and which are alkalis. First ask them to predict the outcomes. They should carry out a fair test to test their predictions, taking care to identify the variables which may be involved. They will need to consider what should stay the same and what will change. How will they measure quantities such as volume of red cabbage water?

Once they have planned their experiment they should carry it out, being careful to record their observations and results systematically. Encourage the children to discuss their results and to make conclusions based on these results.

Investigative skills

The children have asked questions, made predictions and carried out a fair test. They have identified variables and used appropriate equipment to measure volume. They have recorded their results and drawn conclusions.

Content

Red cabbage is a natural indicator which is red when placed in an acid solution, green in an alkaline solution and remains purple when the solution is neutral (i.e. neither acid or alkali). Vinegar is an acid and bicarbonate of soda is an alkali. Acidity and alkalinity are measured on a scale known as the pH scale. This scale runs from 1 to 14 with pH 7 being neutral. pH1 is the strongest acid and pH14 is the strongest alkali.

AT1/4a,4b,4c;
AT3/5b PoS(i)

5. Investigating rust

Age range
Key Stage 2.

Group size
Small groups.

What you need
Test tubes, iron nails, water, salt, paraffin oil.

What to do
This investigation can be introduced with a general discussion on rust and rusting. The children will know about the life of cars being shortened due to rust. They will be aware of the need to look after their bicycles to prevent rust forming.

Where else have they seen rust? Does the formation of rust take place instantly? The children can design an investigation to show the conditions necessary for rusting. They should consider the factors which might be important in the rusting process.

They will need to think about the variables involved and they should carry out a fair test. What will stay the same, what will they change, and how will they know when rusting has taken place?

Each group should be given four test tubes and four nails. If they decide water might be a key factor in the rusting process they could decide whether nails rust in the presence and absence of water. They may decide salt has an effect on rusting (cars are in danger of rusting after being driven on salted roads in the winter). How could the children test the effect of salt on the nails? You may need to suggest that contact with air is important. How could the children exclude air from the nails? (At a later point it will need to be explained that it is the oxygen in the air which is a key factor in rust formation.) Several possibilities could be tried. A nail could be placed in each test tube and conditions varied in the test tubes as described below:
• nail in air-free water – boiled water with paraffin oil on top of it;
• nail in tap water;
• nail in air (nail in test tube with no water);
• nail in water with some salt added.
Observations should be made over a period of a few days.

How will the children record their results? Which nail has rusted the most? How can this be explained? Are any of the nails free from rust? What explanations are most likely for the differences observed?

Investigative skills

The children have formulated hypotheses on the basis of some scientific knowledge (iron rusts when in contact with water and oxygen). They have considered different explanations for the rusting of iron under different conditions and drawn conclusions.

Content

Both oxygen and water are necessary for rusting to take place. Iron reacts with oxygen and water to form iron oxide. This is a red-brown substance which is called rust. Other chemicals such as salt can speed up the rusting process. Boiling the water removes the oxygen in the water.

Rusting can be prevented by excluding oxygen and water. This can be done in a number of ways, for example, painting the iron surface, covering the iron with a layer of oil or grease, coating the iron with a layer of zinc (known as galvanising) or covering the iron with a layer of plastic.

AT1/5a,5c; AT3/5c PoS(iii)

6. How much do I use in a day?

Age range
Key Stage 2.

Group size
Whole class, small groups, or individuals.

What you need
Paper, pencils, rulers, photocopiable page 181.

What to do
This activity can be introduced through a discussion on how dependent we are on water. We could not survive without it. It is useful, therefore, for children to consider how much water they use every day.

The activity will help children to develop the skills of data collection and enable them to record this data in appropriate forms, for example, charts and simple tables. They may then go on to draw bar charts or line graphs to illustrate their results. Ask the children how much water they use at home every day. What do we use water for? As a class, generate a list of ways in which we use water, for example, baths, showers, drinks, cooking, flushing the toilet, washing our clothes,

cleaning our teeth. Ask the children to design an investigation to discover the total amount of water used per day by a family or an individual.

The children could then work in groups to plan how they are going to collect their data. They will need to carry out their investigation at a weekend and will need the cooperation of the family. (Average amounts of water used for different activities are supplied on photocopiable page 181.) The children will not be able to give exact amounts of water used – these will only be average figures but will be appropriate for the purpose of this activity.

They should design a chart or table on which to record their data. They should include on their table the number of times in the day which they used the water for a particular purpose. Photocopiable page 181 shows an example of such a table if the children wish to use it. The group should also consider how they are going to calculate total amounts of water used and how they could represent their results to share with the rest of the class, for example, bar charts, graphs, drawings. Did they use more water than they expected? What can they do to save water? Discuss the severe problems of drought in countries such as Ethiopia and water shortages in parts of Great Britain.

Investigative skills
The children have collected data and recorded this data in charts or simple tables in a systematic way. They have represented their results in the form of bar charts or graphs.

Content
Water is essential for life. The average amount of water used per person per day is 130 litres. The water supplied to our homes needs to be treated to make it fit for consumption.

Instruction books which accompany washing machines and dishwashers usually indicate how much water the machines use.

AT1 PoS; AT2 PoS(i)

7. Whole investigation – Ice cubes melting

Age range
Key Stage 1.

Group size
Small groups.

What you need
Ice cubes, saucers, stop clocks.

What to do
How do I introduce the investigation?
This investigation could be stimulated by seasonal weather conditions – either during freezing winter weather as part of a topic on winter, or during the hot summer months when we put ice in drinks to make them more refreshing.

What questions might the children ask and what hypotheses might they make? The children will have seen ice cubes melting and should be encouraged to ask some of the following questions.
• How long does an ice cube take to melt?
• Can I make the ice cube melt more quickly?
• Can I stop an ice cube from melting?

Firstly the children might time how long an ice cube takes to melt on a saucer in the classroom. They may then go on to place saucers containing ice cubes in different positions – in the shade, in a fridge, in the sunlight, on a window sill above a radiator. Encourage them to test out such predictions as 'The ice cube in the sunlight will melt more quickly than the one in the shade.' **(AT1/2a)**

What observations might the children make?
The children should make close observations of the ice cubes as they melt. The ice cube may look 'frosty' and dry at first. Which part of the ice cube melts first? Are there any patterns or lines on the ice cube? **(AT1/1a,2b)**

Designing the investigation, variables involved, fair testing, testing the prediction.
The children should work in groups and with help and guidance, discuss how they can 'make an ice cube melt more quickly'. How can they make their test fair? Is it fair if some children use different-sized ice cubes? How are they going to measure the time it takes for the ice cubes to melt? How often should they 'inspect' their ice cubes to see if they have melted? What part will each member of the group take in the investigation?

How will the children record their findings?
The children could draw pictures of their ice cubes and write down their observations of the melting ice cubes next to their pictures.

They should record the time it took for each ice cube to melt.

Interpreting the results.
The children should be able to conclude that the ice cubes placed in the sunlight (warmest place) melted at a faster rate than those placed in the shade or in the fridge (cooler places).

They should be encouraged to discuss their observations of the ice cubes during the melting process **(AT1/2c)**

What else might the children investigate?
The children could investigate ice balloons, making observations as they melt. They could explore the effect of salt on the rate of melting.

Content
Water can exist in three forms – a liquid, a vapour (steam) and a solid (ice). Water freezes at 0°C to form ice. When water freezes and changes to ice it expands. This is why pipes sometimes burst in winter. **(AT3/2b PoS(iii))**

CHAPTER 9

Light and sound

The mysteries of light and colour, sound and music have always captured children's imagination. The scientific investigations in this chapter will help children interpret the wonders they will encounter when they look in the mirror, listen to a musical instrument or see shadows cast on the playground on a sunny day.

In the early stages, the children could carry out a simple investigation to find out which materials light will pass through. They can explore the production of shadows and experiment with colour filters. Through making a yoghurt pot telephone children can investigate how sound travels. They will learn about the reflection of light and use this knowledge to make a simple periscope. A whole investigation on vibrating strings will lead to the understanding that sounds are made when objects vibrate, and that the pitch and loudness of these sounds depend on the length and tension of the vibrating string. Children will gain a fuller understanding of light and sound through practising and using those investigative skills which are essential to the activities.

BACKGROUND

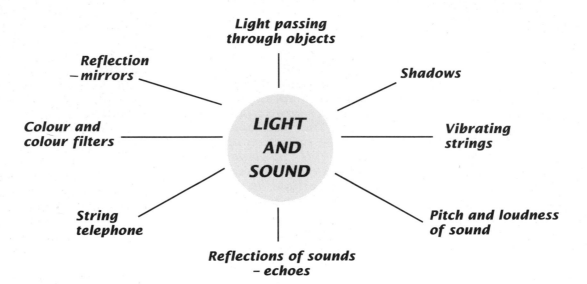

Activity	AT1	Statement of Attainment
1. Light passes through	1a 2a	– Observe – Predict
2. Investigating shadows	3a	– Question, predict.
3. Who's calling?	3a 3c	– Suggest ideas – Carry out a fair test
4. What colour is it?	2a 3a	– Predict – Predict
5. Investigating mirrors – make a periscope	3b 3d	– Observe – Explain
6. Reflecting sound	3a 3b 3c	– Suggest ideas – Observe – Carry out a fair test
7. Whole investigation – vibrating strings	Level 4	

ACTIVITIES

1. Light passes through

Age range
Key Stage 1.

Group size
Pairs or small groups.

What you need
A collection of objects, some translucent, some transparent, and some opaque – for example, empty jars, empty plastic bottles, a variety of plastic egg cartons, empty margarine tubs, sweet wrappers, (a variety – some of the coloured transparent type), plastic food containers, and so on.

What to do
Ask the children to name some everyday materials or objects which they can see through. Working in small groups, the children should choose a number of objects from the collection provided and investigate whether light passes through the materials. This can be done most easily by holding them up to the light. They should predict whether the objects will be transparent, translucent or opaque *before* they test them. They could make a chart to show what they have found out. The results can be grouped into:
• lets all light through;
• lets some light through;
• lets no light through.
Ask the children to draw a picture of each object in the appropriate column on the chart.

Investigative skills
The children have observed familiar materials and predicted which objects the light will pass through.

Content
Light passes through some materials and not others. Materials are *transparent* when light can pass straight through them, for example, clear glass. Objects which reflect nearly all the light that falls on them are said to be *opaque*, for example, wood, paper. *Translucent* materials reflect some light but also let some light through them, which is scattered in all directions, for example, thick plastic, frosted glass. Objects look blurred when viewed through translucent materials.

AT1/1a,2a; AT4/2d

2. Investigating shadows

Age range
Key Stage 1.

Group size
Pairs or small groups.

What you need
Torch, slide projector or overhead projector, a collection of everyday objects which can be used to cast shadows.

What to do
Discuss with the children when they might see shadows being formed. If it is a sunny day, go outside into the school playground with the children to investigate their own shadows. Who has the longest shadow? In which direction are the shadows lying? Do the length and position of the shadows vary at different times of the day? Why are the shadows formed? Ask the children to investigate the formation of shadows in the classroom using a light source such as a torch, slide projector or overhead projector. (This work is preferably done in a darker part of the classroom.) The children should first use a variety of everyday objects and investigate the shadows these objects make by placing the object between the light source and a screen or wall. Encourage the children to raise questions concerning the size of the shadows on the screen. What happens to the shadows when the distance of the object from the light source is changed? How can shadows be made sharper in focus? Does it make a difference if the light source is moved rather than the object?

The children should then test their ideas.

Investigative skills
The children have suggested questions, ideas and predictions and tested these.

Content
Light travels in straight lines. Shadows are formed when some rays of light continue to travel in straight lines while other rays are blocked by an object or person. The size of the shadow depends on the distance between the light source and the object. When the object is near to the light source, it blocks out a lot of light and so the shadow is large. When the object is further away from the light source, it blocks out less light so the shadow is smaller.

AT1/3a; AT4/2d PoS(iv)

3. Who's calling?

Age range
Key Stage 2.

Group size
Pairs.

What you need
Yoghurt pots, strings/threads of various types, a thin nail.

What to do
This activity could be introduced through a discussion on communication – how, in this modern world, we rely so much on the telephone.

Ask the children to work in pairs to make a telephone using the yoghurt pots and string/thread provided. They will need to make a small hole in the bottom of each pot with a thin nail. The string should then be threaded through the holes and secured with a knot. One of the yoghurt pots is the mouthpiece of the telephone and the other is the earpiece.

Ask the children to try and use the telephone – one child should talk into one yoghurt pot while her partner holds the other pot next to his ear and listens. The children could predict that their telephone will only work if the string is taut and whether they can use it 'around corners'. They should make sure that they carry out a fair test and are aware of the variables involved.

Investigative skills

The children have suggested ideas and tested them. They have carried out a fair test and identified variables.

Content

The string must be kept taut. The child's voice makes the air vibrate. These vibrations pass along the string and the voice is heard through the second yoghurt pot.

Further activity

Other inventions such as the loudspeaker could be discussed in the same context that is, the sound is transmitted by making the air vibrate.

AT1/3a,3c; AT4/5f PoS(iv)

4. What colour is it?

Age range

Key Stage 1 and 2.

Group size

Pairs or small groups.

What you need

Coloured acetate sheets, thin card of different colours (including white card) scissors, torch, a selection of different-coloured objects, for example, LEGO bricks.

What to do

Ask the children to carry out an investigation to see what colour objects appear when viewed through the coloured acetate sheets. They could work in groups and each group could cover the end of a torch with a coloured acetate sheet and shine the torch on different-coloured objects. Ask the children to predict, for example, what colour a red

object will look when viewed using a blue acetate sheet. They could cut out shapes from the coloured card and view these through different coloured filters. Again, they should predict the colours the shapes will appear to be.

The children could record their results as shown below. Make a chart from each coloured acetate sheet and stick the coloured shapes on to the chart.

Investigative skills

The children have made predictions and communicated their results in the form of a chart.

▲ The red shape looked...

■ The white shape looked...

● The blue shape looked...

Content

Light is a combination of colours called the spectrum. A red filter will only let red light pass through it. A red object appears to be red because it reflects the red light in the spectrum. All the other colours are absorbed. A blue object will reflect only blue light but will appear black under a red filter because the blue light does not pass through the filter.

Further activity

Coloured spectacles can be made by making a card spectacle frame and sticking different-coloured acetate sheets over each of the eye holes. Objects of different colours can be viewed through the spectacles.

Write secret messages with coloured felt-tipped pens. The messages when viewed through certain colours, will be invisible.

AT1/2a,3a; AT4 PoS(iv)

5. Investigating mirrors – make a periscope

Age range

Key Stage 2.

Group size

Small groups.

What you need

A collection of mirrors of different sizes (preferably the plastic variety), a ruler, Plasticine or Blu-Tack, a cardboard tube (from the inside of a kitchen towel roll), scissors.

What to do

The activity could be introduced with a discussion on shiny and non-shiny objects. Which objects produce the best reflections?

The children should use the mirrors to investigate reflections, starting off looking at their own reflections. If they touch their left ear, which ear is their reflection touching? How can they use the mirrors to reflect objects behind them or round corners? Can they see the back of their heads using the mirrors?

Ask the children to design and make their own periscope. How many mirrors will they need? They will first need to experiment with the mirrors in order to reach a solution to the problem.

Ask the children to test out their periscopes. Can they see

over the top of the tables or other furniture if they are crouched on the floor? Can they see round corners? Do they have to change the position of their periscope to do this?

Investigative skills
The children have made observations, described what they have observed and explained how it happened.

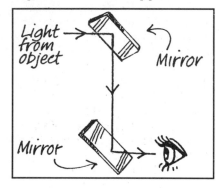

Content
Light travels in straight lines. Light hitting a plane mirror is reflected. A periscope uses two plane mirrors which are tilted at an angle of 45°. One mirror should be placed at the top of the ruler or tube and the other at the bottom. The top mirror reflects light rays from the object which is out of sight down to the bottom mirror which in turn reflects light into the eye.

AT1/3b,3d; AT4/3d PoS(iv)

6. Reflecting sound

Age range
Key Stage 2.

Group size
Pairs, small groups.

What you need
Wrist watch, stop-clock, long cardboard tubes (insides of aluminium foil rolls), a large stiff piece of thick card, metal tray, a soft cushion.

What to do
Introduce the activity with a discussion about echoes. The children will no doubt have tried to make echoes with their voices by shouting loudly into an enclosed space, for example, a tunnel. A watch or clock and a cardboard tube can be used to show how sound is reflected. Ask the children to listen to the sound of a ticking clock or watch. They should then place it a short distance away on a table or flat surface so the sound (only just) cannot be heard. One of the children should hold one end of the tube near the watch and put the other end near his/her ear. The ticking should be clearly heard again.

An investigation can then be set up using two cardboard tubes and the piece of card to find out the best conditions for sound reflection. One child should hold the card up and the tubes should be placed near to, but not touching, the card as shown in this diagram.

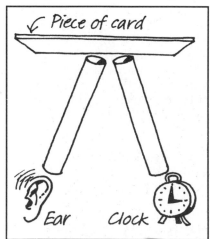

The ticking clock or watch should be placed at one end of one of the tubes and the listener should put his/her ear at the end of the other tube.

The children could:
• try using different surfaces other than card to see which substances reflect the ticks and which absorb them;
• try changing the angle between the cardboard tubes to see whether this makes any difference to the loudness of the sound heard.

How will the children record their results? They might make a table or chart or they could talk about their findings to the rest of the class.

Investigative skills
The children will have suggested questions, ideas and predictions, made observations and will have carried out a fair test. (Does a metal tray reflect the sound as well as a piece of card?)

Content
Echoes are examples of the reflection of sound. Sound is reflected from surfaces in a similar way to a mirror reflecting light.

Sound waves from the ticking clock or watch travel down the tube by hitting the sides of the tube and being reflected by them. The sound thus travels down the tube with very little loss of intensity.

In the investigation with two tubes, the sound travels down one tube, hits the card, and is reflected from the card down the second tube. Some substances, like card, reflect the sound, whereas other substances will absorb or transmit the sound. The children could try using a metal tray or a cushion as alternatives to the card.

AT1/3a,3b,3c; AT4/3d PoS(iv)

7. Whole investigation – investigating vibrating strings

Age range
Key Stage 2.

Group size
Small groups.

What you need
Elastic bands of different thicknesses and various lengths, a shoe box or tissue box, pieces of wood (same width as box and approximately 1–2cm thick), thick cord or nylon thread, pin, plastic tub (large yoghurt or cream carton or margarine tub), marbles, small stones or weights.

How do I introduce the investigation?
The children will have been investigating musical instruments to see how sounds are made. They will have seen and played a range of familiar instruments, for example, guitar, drum, recorder, xylophone; they will now know that sounds are made by vibrating objects. When a guitar string is stretched and plucked, the string vibrates and a sound is produced.

What questions might the children ask and what hypotheses might they make?
Discuss the stringed instruments which the children have seen and encourage the children to question how notes of different pitch are made. Why does one guitar sound different from another? How are loud and soft sounds produced? Introduce the idea of the 'pitch' of the sound.

Do stretched, thick elastic bands make different sounds from thinner bands when 'plucked'? If a cord/thread is stretched how could the sound it makes when plucked be changed to make it sound higher or lower?

The children might first explore sounds made by plucking stretched elastic bands of different thicknesses. They can then go on to test out their hypotheses such as 'Plucking thicker elastic bands produces lower notes.' or 'The amount the band is stretched affects the pitch of the note.'

The investigation can then be taken further, for example, 'How can we change the pitch of the sound produced by a vibrating elastic band or string?' or 'How does changing the length/tension of the vibrating string affect the pitch of the note?' *(AT1/4a)*

What observations might the children make?
The children should be encouraged to make observations based on their preliminary investigations of

musical instruments, for example, guitar. How are the strings tightened or loosened? What is causing the sound to be made? What is vibrating?

Designing the investigation, variables involved, fair testing, testing the hypothesis.

The children should work in groups and discuss how they are going to carry out the investigation. They need to ensure that they carry out a 'fair test' and consider which variables are involved. They might wish to use a variety of elastic bands stretched over a box. The elastic bands may need to be held clear of the box by pieces of wood which act like the bridge of a guitar.

They could just experiment with one piece of cord/thread and alter the tension in this cord/thread using a weighted margarine or yoghurt tub. Alternatively they may wish to change the length of the cord by supporting it with two pieces of wood (or two pencils) and alter the distance between these pieces of wood by moving them closer together or further apart.

Whatever method they decide upon it is important

that they identify clearly what will change and what they need to keep the same. It is important for the children to consider at least two variables in this investigation, that is, the tension in the cord (produced by the weights pulling on the cord) and the vibrating length of the cord between the pieces of wood. **(AT1/4b)**

How will the children record their findings?

There are a variety of ways in which the children could record their findings. They might wish to make a collage or chart on which they pin the elastic bands used and relate these to the pitch of the sound, that is, highest note produced to lowest note produced.

Interpreting the result

Encourage the children to offer explanations which link their observations to their original hypothesis, for example, the more stretched the elastic band or cord is, the higher the note will sound *or* the pitch of the note depends on the length of the stretched string or cord. **(AT1/4c)**

What else might the children investigate?

The children could investigate pitch of notes in wind instruments, for example, a bottle organ or music from pipes.

Content

Pitch means how high or how low a sound is. The strings of a guitar are made to vibrate by plucking them with the fingers. The length of the vibrating portion of the string is altered by pressing the fingers down at different points along its length.

In this investigation, as the length of the string/cord between the pieces of wood gets shorter, the pitch of the note will get higher. Tightening the string or elastic band produces a higher note. Thicker elastic bands produce lower notes. **(AT4/5d) PoS(iv)**

CHAPTER 10

Electricity and magnetism

Children experience magents from an early age through games such as magnet fishing and by playing with ornaments which miraculously stick to fridges and other metal objects. They soon become aware of the need for batteries to power their vehicles, games and torches, even if the concept of a circuit is far from their minds.

Through carrying out investigations with magnets, children will develop knowledge and understanding of magnetic and non-magnetic objects, magnetic poles, the pushing and pulling forces involved and the relative strengths of the magnets. At an early stage, children may predict and test whether items are attracted to a magnet or not, before developing their ideas on magnetic poles. Rules such as 'like poles repel' and 'unlike poles attract' may be discovered or verified by investigation. At a later stage, children may carry out a fair test to ascertain the relative strength of the magnets and quantify their results.

After becoming familiar with the concept of a circuit, children may investigate conductors and insulators by predicting and testing which objects will allow a bulb to light in such a circuit. They should establish that metals will conduct electricity, which offers a basis for further investigations such as, 'Will all metals conduct electricity?' Later, the children may vary the flow of electricity using a two (or more) cell battery. A whole investigation on the strength of electro-magnets incorporates work on magnets and electric circuits. Children are asked to hypothesise about how the electro-magnet may be made stronger, carry out a fair test and compare their results with their prediction. All of these activities help to further children's knowledge of magnetism and electricity, as well as develop their investigative skills.

BACKGROUND

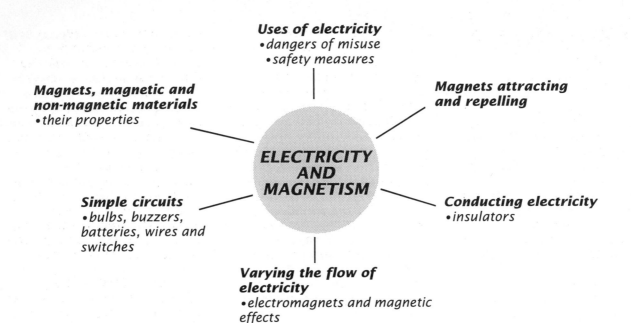

Uses of electricity
- *dangers of misuse*
- *safety measures*

Magnets, magnetic and non-magnetic materials
- *their properties*

Magnets attracting and repelling

ELECTRICITY AND MAGNETISM

Conducting electricity
- *insulators*

Simple circuits
- *bulbs, buzzers, batteries, wires and switches*

Varying the flow of electricity
- *electromagnets and magnetic effects*

Activity	AT1	Statement of Attainment
1. Electricity may be very dangerous!	1a	– Observe
2. Exploring with magnets	1a, 2b PoS	– Observe
3. Which way will the magnet car travel?	2a	– Ask questions, suggest ideas
4. Which is the strongest magnet?	3a 3b	– Suggest questions – Observe, measure
5. I'll conduct, you insulate	2a, 3a	– Ask questions, predict
6. Measuring an electric current	4a, 5a 4b 4c	– Predict, hypothesise – Measure, fair test – Interpret results
7. Whole investigation – the strength of electromagnets	Levels 3 and 4	

ACTIVITIES

1. Electricity may be very dangerous!

Age range
Key Stage 1.

Group size
Individual and whole class.

What you need
Photocopiable page 182, torch, other battery powered items.

What to do
Talk to the children about items in their classroom and at home which use electricity (electrical energy). They might think about many of the items with flexes but forget some of the others, for example, cookers, electric lights. Ask them where electricity comes from and try to make some link between power stations, pylons and wires coming into the house.

Talk to them about the dangers of electricity in a general sense. Give them photocopiable page 182 and ask them to name the electrical item and to ring or write about the danger in the picture.

Talk to the class about the real dangers if electrical items are misused, highlighting the points brought out by the pictures. Stress that nothing but properly wired up plugs should be put in plug sockets and that no electrical item should be used near water, or outside on a wet day.

Explain that battery-powered items are not so dangerous except for large batteries, for example, car batteries.

Investigative skills
The children will have been given the opportunity to observe everyday items in the classroom and at home which may be dangerous.

Content
The children should be introduced to the idea that many items in their classroom, school and home use electricity and if not used properly are dangerous. They should also be introduced to electrical items which are powered by batteries and appreciate that these may not be so dangerous but should be still treated with respect. Car batteries may cause severe burns and a nasty shock.

Try to use the term 'electrical energy' when appropriate, to illustrate that electricity is just one type of the many forms of energy.

Further activities
Ask the children to make a list or draw pictures of some of the items at home which use electricity.

Safety
Children should be made aware that misuse of any electrical item may be dangerous.

AT1/1a; AT4/1a

2. Exploring with magnets

Age range
Key Stage 1.

What you need
Magnets, a given number of objects and materials or objects in the classroom.

What to do
Children should be encouraged to bring examples of magnets from home. These could be from toy kits or be ornaments found on the fridge, freezer or metal notice-board.

Initially ask the children to explore and investigate objects and materials with their magnets (see Safety section).

After sufficient time, ask the children to talk about what they have found out. They should be able to inform you that the magnet 'stuck to' or was 'pulled to' or 'pulled' certain objects. They may tell you that some objects could be lifted off the table while others could not.

Encourage the children to divide the objects into two sets, those which 'stick' to magnets (attracted by magnets) and those which do not. Encourage the children to use the word *attract*.
Where have the children seen magnets used in and around the home? What about outside the home?

Investigative skills
The children have 'observed familiar objects (and events)' and you have 'promoted at first hand the exploration of materials'.

Content
Magnets attract some materials and not others. The children have explored the effects of magnets on a variety of magnetic and non-magnetic materials and have considered their uses to close cupboard and fridge doors, to hold up paper on fridge doors and metal boards.

Safety
Magnets may cause damage to electrical items such as television sets, video recorders and so on. Ensure that the children do not experiment near these items.

AT1/1a,2b PoS; AT4/2a PoS

3. Which way will the magnet car travel?

Age range
Key Stage 1.

Group size
Pairs.

What you need
Two plastic-coated red and blue coloured magnets per pair; a light, plastic car with magnet attached to it with, sticky tape.

What to do
Allow the children to explore with the two magnets. After the children have done this ask them to try and make a light plastic car move using two magnets (provide them with the sticky tape). If they do not come up with a solution quickly, provide them with a car on to which a magnet has been attached (see below).

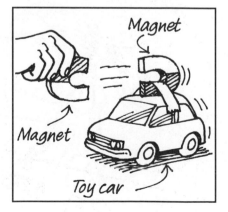

Allow them to explore again using a second magnet. They will hopefully come up with comments such as 'How/why is it moving?' and as they use both ends of the magnet they might be able to predict which way the car will move; 'If I use this (blue) end of the magnet the car will go forward.' and 'I think that if you use the red end of the magnet the car will go backwards.' and 'What will happen if I use two magnets?'

Investigative skills
The children have carried out an investigation in which they have had to '... ask questions such as "How...?", "Why...?", and "What will happen if...?", suggest ideas and make predictions.'

Content
Magnets have two poles, a north facing pole and a south facing pole. When two north poles are held near each other they push each other apart; similarly, when two south poles are held near to each other they push each other away or they *repel* one another. When a north pole of

one magnet and a south pole of another magnet are brought close together they are drawn or *attracted* to each other. Thus, *like poles repel and unlike poles attract* each other.

It is advisable to use red (north pole) and blue (south pole) coloured magnets as this will make the children's explanations and predictions simpler, avoiding such comments as 'When this end is brought near to the magnet.'

Safety
Magnets may cause damage to electrical items such as television sets, video recorders, etc. Ensure that the children *do not* experiment near these items.

AT1/2a; AT4/2a

4. Which is the strongest magnet?

Age range
Key Stage 1 and 2.

Group size
Pairs.

What you need
Different types of magnets; paper clips; paper clip suspended on a piece of cotton; ruler.

What to do
Allow the children to investigate with a number of

different types of magnets and a variety of objects. They will soon find some of the magnets are stronger than others and may begin to make comments like 'This long red magnet is strongest'. Get them to pose questions such as 'Which magnet is the strongest?' or 'Is it true that the bigger the magnet the stronger it will be?'. Challenge them to design an investigation to see if it is in keeping with their idea (hypothesis). Produce the paper clips if the children are finding difficulties. Ask them to record their results and to comment on whether they have set up a fair test.

Alternatively, after the children have posed a question, provide them with the apparatus illustrated below. They will soon see that as they move the magnet slowly towards the paper clip it will be attracted and start to move. They should record the distance from the magnet to the suspended paper clip (in the vertical position). Repeat this three times and take the average or the median result. Repeat for the other magnets.

Investigative skills
The children will have suggested a question and may have made a prediction based on their experience. Measurement involving instruments is not involved and the variables involved in the fair test are very simple (independent variable = types of magnets; dependent variable = number of paper clips attracted to magnets) unless a variety of sizes of paperclips are available and selection is needed. In the latter case AT1/3b might be achieved.

The children in the second example will have suggested a

question and may have made a prediction based on their experience. They will also have quantified their result by measuring using a ruler.

Content
Some magnets have more magnetic energy than others and are therefore able to attract more items, or more mass of items to them. While this may be 'felt' it can be verified through testing.

Safety
Magnets may cause damage to electrical items such as television sets, videos and tape recorders.

AT1/3a,3b

5. I'll conduct, you insulate

Age range
Key Stage 1 and 2.

Group size
Pairs.

What you need
Simple circuit (see below), consisting of a battery (cell), three pieces of wire and a bulb holder containing a 1.5 or 2.5 volt bulb, photocopiable page 183. Two of the pieces of wire will preferably contain a crocodile clip at one end.

What to do
Show the children the circuit and remind them that a complete circuit is needed for the electricity to flow and for the bulb to light. Select two items, one which conducts electricity, e.g. a paper clip and one which does not conduct electricity, e.g. a rubber eraser. Place each in turn in the circuit and get the children to tell you what happens; 'The bulb lights when the paper clip is in the circuit but does not light when the rubber is in the circuit'.

Allow the children to investigate safely for a few minutes using items in the classroom, then present them with ten or more items which they might not have experienced directly. Point out that the items are made of different materials which have different properties. Give the children photocopiable page 183 and first ask them to predict, then test, whether each item will make the bulb light up when placed in the circuit. When they have completed this, ask them to compare their predictions (what they thought would happen) with their test results (what actually happened).

Finally ask the children to explain their results. Can they see a pattern arising from the materials they used?

Investigative skills
The children will be asking questions such as 'What will happen if I put a ruler in the gap between the wires?' and will be making predictions about which materials or objects will make the bulb light up.

They will have compared their results with their predictions. Some may be able to see that when the metal objects are placed in the circuit, the bulb lights because 'the electricity is passing through them unlike the other objects'. Here, the children have given a simple explanation of why certain objects, when placed in the circuit, cause the bulb to light.

Content
The children will have gained experience of simple circuits containing a battery, bulb and wires. They will also have investigated materials finding out whether they conduct electricity or not.

Safety
The children should be reminded that while the batteries and circuits used in science activities are safe to touch, other electrical circuits at home and at school are very dangerous if misused.

AT1/2a,3a; AT4 PoS(i)

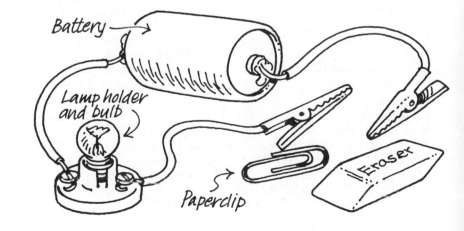

6. Measuring an electric current

Age range
Key Stage 2.

Group size
Pairs.

What you need
Batteries (up to 5), sellotape or cardboard tube to keep batteries in electrical contact, 6 volt lamp (bulb) in lamp holder, ammeter (instrument for measuring electrical current) or voltmeter (instrument for measuring the electrical push driving the current around a circuit – see Figure 1 below), 3 wires.

Figure 1

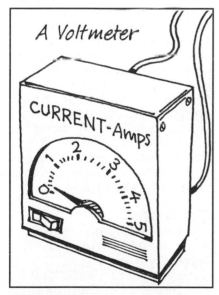

A Voltmeter

CURRENT-Amps

What to do
Allow the children to use the ammeters and/or voltmeters to measure the electric current and the electrical push from the batteries in their normal work with electricity. They should have gained some knowledge relating to the number of batteries (cells) and the size of current and size of electrical push. They should have also been introduced to knowledge of current and electrical push in simple terms (see below). Remind the children of the work they have done with circuits and the use of ammeters. Show the children the apparatus and tell them that today they may use up to 5 cells. What question would they like to ask and investigate?

Investigative skills
If a child responds to your question in a manner such as, 'I'd like to see if the number of cells affects the current', ask them to put this comment into the form of a prediction, stating a reason. They might say that 'The more batteries there are the bigger the current because there will be more electricity or electrons. Alternatively, some children may respond that 'More cells will produce a larger current as there is more energy in the circuit the more cells there are'. Here, a hypothesis has been made and a causal link stated, based on scientific theory.

Ask the children to test their predictions and hypotheses and to record their results in tables and on graphs. (Level 5b cannot be achieved because the independent variable is not continuous).

The children should be able to relate their results to their conclusions and identify a pattern such as, 'The more cells the higher the current.' They might be asked to consider why their graph was not a straight line. This could be related to the pushing power/energy of some cells being less than others.

Content
A cell changes chemical energy into electrical energy. A *battery* is made by putting two or more cells together. Hence, a single 'battery' should really be referred to as a 'cell'.

Electric current is a flow of electrons. The electrons are pushed away from the negative side of the battery towards the positive side. The current in a circuit is measured in amperes (amps – A) after the French physicist Andre Ampere (1775–1836), and it indicates the rate at which charge (electrons) is flowing. You can get a rough idea of the size of an electric current by seeing how brightly it lights a bulb. But a quantitative measurement may be obtained with an ammeter. The current is the same at all points around a simple circuit. It is not used up by a bulb/ lamp or buzzer. The driving force or electrical push in a circuit is called the *voltage*. It is measured in volts with a special meter called a *voltmeter*. Voltmeters measure the push, driving the current around a circuit. The cell or battery gives potential energy to the electrons and it is this *energy* that is lost, as heat and light, as the electrons pass through the bulbs.

Gradually, the cell/battery loses its pushing ability and the current can no longer flow.

Safety
The children should be reminded that while the batteries and circuits used in science activities produce and use a relatively small electrical current and push, and hence are safe to touch, other electrical circuits at home and at school are dangerous if misused owing to the large electrical push and current.

AT1/4a,4b,4c,5a

7. Whole investigation – the strength of electromagnets

Age range
Key Stage 2 (Levels 3 and 4).

Group size
Pairs.

What you need
Batteries, wires, crocodile clips, a switch, iron nails or iron rods of different sizes, paper clips.

What to do
How do I introduce the investigation?
Show the children a simple circuit containing a two-celled battery, a switch and an electromagnet. An electromagnet may be constructed by winding insulated wire around the nail as shown below. Show the children that when a complete circuit is made the electromagnet will pick up a paper clip, but when the circuit is broken the paper clip is soon released by the iron nail (electromagnet). Explain that the electromagnet works because as the electric current passes through the wire, the nail becomes a temporary magnet. Remind the children to disconnect the circuit as soon as they have taken a result in order to maintain the voltage (pushing power) of the battery.

Discuss with the children where they have seen electromagnets on television and in the locality. Examples such as scrap yards and electric bells might be given.

What questions might the children ask and what hypotheses might they make?
Discuss with the children the possible variables (factors) which might make the electromagnet stronger or weaker. They might suggest:
- number of batteries;
- number of turns of the wire;
- length of nail;
- width of wire;
- length of wire;
- width (gauge) of wire.

Encourage the children to think of one of the factors to investigate. Ask them to think about and *write down* a prediction/hypothesis for their investigation, such as 'The greater the number of turns of the wire, the more paper clips will be picked up because the electromagnet is stronger.' *(AT1/3a, 4a)*

Designing the investigation, fair testing, testing the hypothesis.
Remind the children to carry out a fair test and to use an appropriate range for their variable, for example, ten, twenty, thirty, forty, fifty turns of the wire. *(AT1/3b)*

How will the children record their findings?
Get them to record their results in a manner that they see as suitable (a table). Some children might be encouraged to display their results on a bar chart or histogram.

Interpreting the results.
After the children have completed their investigation get them to look for a pattern in their results. How does this pattern fit in with their original prediction/hypothesis? Is the pattern regular? Why might this not be so (not enough readings taken for each range of the factor [variable] or not a fair test)? *(AT1/4c)*

Content
Children should be reminded that a complete circuit is necessary to get the electromagnet to work. This may be reinforced during the introduction to the investigation. *(AT4/3a)*

Safety
Remind the children that while this type of circuit is not dangerous, the mains electricity in the home and at school, and large batteries (car batteries) are dangerous. *(AT4 PoS(i))*

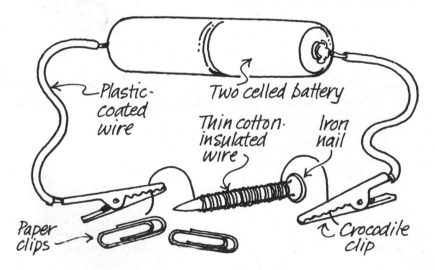

Plastic-coated wire
Two celled battery
Thin cotton-insulated wire
Iron nail
Paper clips
Crocodile clip

CHAPTER 11

Forces

From a very early age children throw toys out of their pram and grab their parents' hair! In so doing, they are showing practical examples of how pushing and pulling forces may be applied. All ball games involve pushing forces and often pulling forces. Walking the dog involves a pulling force, whether it is you or the dog being pulled! Moving a pram or a supermarket trolley involves a pushing force.

At Key Stage 1, children should investigate the pushing and pulling forces in everyday contexts and get used to using terms 'push or pushing force' and 'pull or pulling force'. Bicycles are excellent to investigate as sitting on the saddle, braking, pedalling and changing gear all involve forces. Later, the children may explore the forces involved with balloon propulsion and measure the forces exerted by various objects.

The forces involved when objects sink and float may be investigated and measured at Key Stage 2. Children are encouraged to look for inaccuracies in their methods (unfair tests) and to comment on why things happened. Bridge building, which might incorporate work in technology, is both motivating to children and will heighten knowledge and understanding of forces. The whole investigation considers the effect of movement of an object over different surfaces, which exert different amounts of that interesting force, friction. The activities carried out by children on the topic of forces are ideal to develop the investigative skills of questioning, hypothesising, fair testing and inferring.

BACKGROUND

Pushes and pulls
•movement by start
moving/stop moving
•speeding up/slowing
down

FORCES

Forces
•affect the postion, movement
and shape of object
•act in different directions
•size and direction affects
movement

Activity	AT1	Statement of Attainment
1. Pushes and pulls	1a	– Observe
2. The pushes and pulls of riding a bicycle	2b	– Observe
3. Balloon propulsion	3a 3b	– Question and predict – Measure
4. How much force?	3b	– Measure
5. Forces (upthrust) in water	3b 3c, 3d	– Observe and measure – Interpret and evaluate
6. Bridge building	3a, 4a 4b 3d, 4c	– Question and predict – Observe, measure, fair test – Interpret
7. Whole investigation – surfaces and friction	Level 5	

ACTIVITIES

1. Pushes and pulls

Age range
Key Stage 1.

Group size
Individuals.

What you need
Photocopiable page 184; various objects which the children may push and pull.

What to do
Introduce the children to 'pushes' and 'pulls' through a story or poem or real-life experiences such as pushing a supermarket trolley or pram or pulling a toy on a string. Get a model pram or a car and give it a 'push'. Now give the object a 'pull'. Repeat this activity with other objects and see if the children can show you examples.

Give out photocopiable page 184 and explain to the children that they must identify whether a 'push' or a 'pull' is being exerted, by writing 'push' or 'pull' alongside the pictures or by colouring the pushes one colour and the pulls another colour.

Investigative skills
The children have made observations on events and incidents in a scientific context.

Content
The children will have been introduced to pushing and pulling forces through a number of everyday examples. They should be made aware that things do not start to move until they are given a push or a pull.

You could encourage the children to use the words 'pulling force' and 'pushing force' in readiness for later work.

Further activity
Place a piece of paper or a biro in your fingers and without excess movement release it and allow it to fall to the ground. Ask the children if a push or a pull is involved here. If they do not know or say neither, explain that there must be one of the two because the object is moving. They might think that a push is involved because you are pushing it away from you, so make it clear that you are just letting it drop. Explain that there is a pulling force in the Earth which explains why things go downwards and not upwards when they are dropped. This is a difficult concept, but this example provides a basis for children's understanding of gravity. Let the children experience the pulling force involved.

Safety
Ensure that safe light objects are dropped and that pushes and pulls are not too excessively applied.

AT1/1a; AT4/1b,2c

2. The pushes and pulls of riding a bicycle

Age range
Key Stage 1 and 2.

Group size
Whole class working individually or in pairs.

What you need
Pram or toy on a string, bicycle, photocopiable page 185, crayon.

What to do
Show the children the pram or toy on a string and ask them why it is not moving. Ask them whether there are any pushes and pulls acting on it. Remind them that the pull of the Earth pulls everything to the floor (towards the centre of the Earth).

Ask the children how they could make the pram or toy move. They might think of a push but not a pull. Use the words 'pushing force' and 'pulling force'. Push and then pull the pram or toy across the floor and ask the children how it could be made to go faster. They should now realise that pushes and pulls can speed things up. Repeat the activity but now ask the children how they could slow the pram or toy down (but not stop it).

Finally, ask the children how they could stop the objects. Are they using a pushing or a pulling force?

Show the children photocopiable page 185 and an actual bicycle. Get the children to explain the various parts. Explain to the children that they are going to label or colour all the pushes and pulls when someone is riding a bicycle. Some of these help to start the bicycle moving and make it go faster while others help to slow it down and to stop it.

Investigative skills
By identifying the pushes and pulls, the children have noted a series of related observations of the bicycle.

Content
The children will be beginning to understand that pushes and pulls (pushing and pulling forces) are needed to start things moving and to stop them. They will also be introduced to the idea that pushing and pulling forces slow things down (a bicycle braking) and speed things up (pedalling harder and a bat hitting a ball).

Further activity
Develop the idea further that forces affect the position and

movement of objects. Also develop the idea that pushing and pulling forces can affect the shape of objects by giving children sponges, balls or erasers which they may squeeze, twist, stretch, compress and so on.

Safety
If children are going to ride the bicycle, adequate supervision should be provided in 'safe' areas.

AT1/2b; AT4/2c,3c

3. Balloon propulsion

Age range
Key Stage 1 and 2.

Group size
Small groups.

What you need
Long balloons, pump, cotton or gut, a straw, sticky tape.

What to do
Children will be aware that if they blow up and release a balloon, it propels itself around the room. The force exerted by the escaping air may be controlled using the balloon monorail.
Ask the children to pump up a balloon, and then release it. Does it go far? How can it be made to go further? Does it go in the same direction each time? Does a round balloon travel in the same way as a long one?

The children can then set up the apparatus shown in the diagram above. They should then blow into the balloon and pinch the end with their fingers, until they are ready to let go. Ask the children how the balloon could be made to

go further. Ask them how they could test this. How would we know if it has gone further (measurement)? How could we control the amount of energy we give to the balloon (number of puffs or pumps)?

Investigative skills
To complete the above task successfully the children will need to observe closely and quantify by measuring using appropriate instruments such as rulers. The children will also need to recognise testable questions, ideas and predictions.

Content
Energy is stored in the balloon (stored or *potential* energy). Movement (push) occurs in the opposite direction to the thrust of the air escaping. A similar phenomenon causes movement in a space rocket or jet engine.

Safety
Set up the cotton or gut line in a corner of the classroom, preferably slightly above head height. Ensure that it is taken down or made conspicuous when not in use.

AT1/3a,3b; AT4/2c,3c

4. How much force?

Age range
Key Stage 1 and 2.

Group size
Small groups.

What you need
Various objects which may be pulled when connected to a newton meter.

What to do
Explain to the children that a newton meter is an instrument to measure forces, particularly pulling forces. Show them the scale and see if they can read it accurately. Some newton meters have a device to show the maximum force applied and this has to be shaken down to zero before the next reading is taken.

Ask the children to record in a table the force needed to move or raise the various objects (see the table below).

Object	Force needed to move it

Investigative skills
The children have used a newton meter to measure the force applied to an object.

Content
Weight is a force which is measured in newtons (N). Objects exert a force due to the Earth's gravitational pull. A 1kg mass exerts a force of approximately 10 newtons; a 100g object will exert a force of approximately 1 newton.

The children have explored various forces and have compared the differences in the size of forces needed to move objects and to raise them above the ground.

Object	Weight (mass)	Force (newtons = N)

Figure 1

Further activity
The children could be given various objects, measuring scales (kg and g) and a newton meter. Encourage them to find through accurate measurement the relationship between the weight (mass) of an object and the force it applies. A table like Figure 1, above, will help.

Safety
Ensure that the children take care when lifting objects with the newton meter. A 1kg mass in free fall can damage toes.

AT1/3b; AT4 PoS(iii)

5. Forces (upthrust) in water

Age range
Key Stages 1 and 2.

Group size
Small groups.

What you need
A newton meter, a large transparent beaker of water or similar container, various objects which could be held by a newton meter and immersed totally in the water, cotton or string.

What to do
Show the children the objects and gently lower them one at a time into the water. Ask the children to tell you what has happened. Ask them if there are any forces acting on the objects and what they are. Remind them that the force of gravity is acting downwards but the water is exerting a force upward. Have they ever experienced a force in the water? Have they been propelled to the surface with a polystyrene float at the baths? This force is called *upthrust*.

Select some objects that may be attached to a newton meter; alternatively cotton or string could be tied around the objects so that they may be attached to the meter (see Figure 2 below).

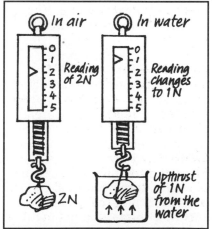

Figure 2

Weigh one of the objects and record its weight (mass). Show the children the apparatus and ask them to predict whether the object will weigh more, the same or less when it is totally submerged in water. Ask them to write down their prediction and why they have suggested it. Lower the same object into the water making sure that it is totally submerged but that as little of the newton meter is in the water as possible. Record its weight again. What do the children notice? Objects appear to lose weight or exert less force when in water, due to a force (upthrust) exerted in the water. Allow the children to investigate using the other objects and perhaps objects of their choice. Ask them to complete a table of results.

Investigative skills

The children have used a newton meter to observe and quantify. Some children might have noticed that individuals' tests were unfair because not all the object was submerged in the water or parts of the newton meter were in the water. Ask the children to write down what happened and to explain why it happened using the words 'force, 'upthrust' and 'gravity'.

Content

This activity will help the children to understand that more than one force can act on an object and that forces act in different directions. Whereas gravity acts downwards on the various objects, a force in the water called upthrust acts on them and tends to push them upwards. If the force of gravity is greater than the force of upthrust then the object will sink, for example, in a ball of Plasticine or a stone. However, if the upthrust (force) acting on an object is equal to the force of gravity, then the object will float. Weight is a force measured in newtons (N). The children will realise that objects which float effectively have a weight of zero in water.

AT1/3b,3c,3d; AT4/3c,4c,5d

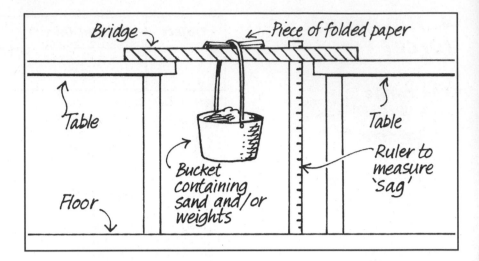

6. Bridge building

Age range
Key Stage 2.

Group size
Pairs.

What you need
A4 'waste' paper, glue, scissors, buckets, sand or gravel or weights (masses), newton meters (1–10N, 1–5N)

What to do
Talk to the children about bridges, raising questions about what they are used for and what needs to be considered when they are designed. Explain to them that they are going to be working as engineers today when they make a small model of a bridge. They will be given one side of A4 paper, glue, and scissors for each constructed bridge. The finished bridge must cross a gap of 15cm and must be free standing (no glue or object can fasten it to the tables which will form the 15cm gap). Show them how the bridges will be tested by placing a bucket attached to a string around the bridge; a piece of A4 paper folded four times could be placed between the bucket handle or string to prevent it from damaging the bridge (see the diagram above). The bucket will then be loaded with sand or gravel or weights (masses). Challenge the children to investigate how to make the strongest bridge.

Ask the children to consider carefully how to make the bridges, to say why they have made each bridge like they have and to predict which will be the strongest.

In their pairs ask them to think about how they will make it a fair test (use the same amount of paper and the same amount of glue – tricky!), ensure the test gap is 15cm for all bridges, that the bucket is set up the same each time and that the sand or gravel is added at the same speed, preferably one cup full of sand every so many seconds.

Ask the children to name their bridge, to draw a diagram of its cross-section, record the force the bridge withstood and record this in a table of results on the board and in their books. Ask them also to record the results of other groups. Finally ask them to consider the results of the class and to make any conclusions relating these to their predictions.

Investigative skills
The children will have suggested ideas and made predictions, based on everyday experience which may be tested or based on relevant knowledge which may be investigated.

Some of the children may have carried out a fair test (see above) and selected the appropriate instrument (newton meter) to measure the force.

The children will have had the opportunity to interpret their findings; they might have observed that the 'tighter' the bridge or, if a triangular bridge was constructed, the stronger it was because tight structures or triangular shapes are stronger. Other children may have pointed out that small (tight), triangular bridges or tightly rolled round (cylindrical) bridges are strongest. These bridges may have withstood forces of 40 newtons but the loose, rectangular bridges would only withstand 7 newtons.

Content
The children will have found out that structures of a certain shape are stronger than others and are therefore capable of withstanding more force than others. Before the bridge collapses there are two main forces acting on it: the force of gravity acting downwards on the bridge and its load and, the force of upthrust/ resistance acting upwards from the bridge. These forces are equal. As their bridge collapses the children will probably see that the ends in contact with the table lift up. At this point the force acting

downwards is greater than the force acting upwards, so the bridge moves and collapses.

Safety
Ensure that there is no danger of the bucket of sand falling on children's feet. This should not happen due to the placing of the tables. Sand should be swept up at the end of the activity to avoid slippery floors.

AT1/3a,3d,4a,4b,4c; AT4/3c,4c,5d

7. Whole investigation – surfaces and friction

Age range
Key Stage 2.

Group size
Pairs or small groups.

What you need
A vehicle with attachment, a large pulley, string and a mass holder, various surfaces (from smooth to rough) including perspex, wood, carpet, sand paper of different grades, or alternatively, newton meters

and blocks of wood to which different surfaces may be adhered; photocopiable page 180.

What to do
How do I introduce the investigation?
Children are familiar with friction through rubbing their hands and experiencing the heat produced and the resistance to movement of one hand as it is rubbed over the other. They will have carried out activities to feel and measure friction, but need to know that it is the force that tries to stop one object from moving or sliding across another. It slows down the moving parts of a machine because they rub together or slide across one another. The force of friction in an engine is reduced by oil, making the surface of the moving parts slippery. However, without friction we could not move, cars could not move and if they did, they would not stop.
What initial observations might the children make?
Show the children the equipment but inform them that they may have other items if required. Allow them to carry out some exploratory trials with their apparatus. They might use one or other of the experimental set-ups, A

Set-up A

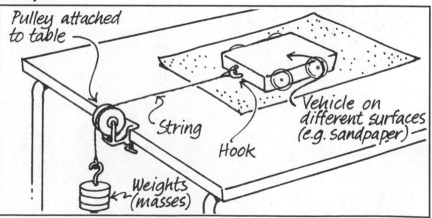

Pulley attached to table

String

Hook

Weights (masses)

Vehicle on different surfaces (e.g. sandpaper)

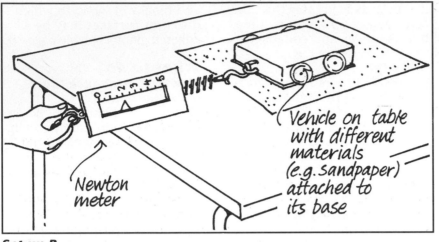

Set-up B

and B. In A, the children will realise that more weights (masses) are needed to move the 'vehicle' if the friction increases. In B, the greater the friction, the higher the reading will be on the newton meter.

What questions might the children ask and what hypotheses might they make?

Ask them to raise a question, prediction or hypothesis which they might like to investigate. Remind them to give a reason for their prediction (causal link), preferably based on scientific knowledge, understanding or theory.

If the children are able to suggest in A that more weights will be needed to to move the vehicle on rougher surfaces because friction increases as the surface becomes rougher, they will be operating at Level 5. **(AT/5a)** To operate at Level 5 in B, the children will need to hypothesise that a greater force (newtons) will be needed to move the vehicle on rough surfaces because as the surface becomes rougher, the rubbing due to friction increases. **(AT1/5a)**

What observations might the children make?

The children will observe the weights (masses) needed to move the vehicle on different surfaces in A and the force due to friction (newtons) in B.

Designing the investigation, variables involved, fair testing, testing the hypothesis.

Hand out photocopiable page 180. Ask them to consider the variable to be systematically changed and the range to be selected, the variable to be measured in the investigation and the variables to be kept constant. Clearly, the vehicle should not be so heavy and the surfaces so rough that an enormous weight or force is required to move it. How many surfaces will they choose? Grades of sandpaper would give a quantitative rather than qualitative range for the independent variable. If the children have carried out a fair test and obtained valid results by choosing a suitable range of variables, they will have achieved Level 5. **(AT1/5b)**

How will the children record their findings?

In A, the children will probably record their results in table form showing that as the roughness of the surface increases, (e.g. sandpaper) the weights (masses) required to move the vehicle will have increased. In B, again a table may be constructed to show the surface used and the amount of force (newtons) required to move the vehicle. Graphs could be drawn if sandpaper was used, plotting weights used or force against the size of particles, as indicated on the back of the sandpaper. **(AT1 PoS)**

Interpreting the results

In A, the children might interpret their results by pointing out that as the surface became rougher, more weights or force were required to move their vehicle because of the increased friction. **(AT1/4c)** If they are also able to suggest a different conclusion and evaluate its validity against the previous one, they will have achieved Level 5. **(AT1/5c)** In this investigation this is not particularly easy.

What else might the children investigate?

The children could investigate the effect of friction of oil between two rough surfaces.

Content

Forces affect the position and movement of an object. **(AT3/3c)** The children should be aware that the force of gravity is acting *downwards* on their vehicle and that the force of friction is attempting to prevent them from moving the vehicle. Thus, more than one force is acting on their vehicle and these forces are pushing and pulling in different directions. **(AT3/4c)** They should be aware that the size and direction of these forces affects the movement of the vehicle. The amount of force in newtons (A) or the weight required to move their vehicle is greater than the force preventing it from moving. **(AT3/5d)**

CHAPTER 12

Ourselves

The topic 'Ourselves' is a familiar one in the primary classroom. It centres on children's own experiences and provides a wealth of opportunities for cross-curricular work. At an early stage, children should find out about themselves and develop ideas about how they grow, use their senses and maintain a fit and healthy body.

Scientific investigations can be introduced in the theme 'Ourselves' through simple observations; for example, measurement of the children's own hands and feet. They will discover similarities and differences between themselves which can be extended into class surveys of eye colour and height. Skills in collecting and recording data will be developed through these activities.

Consideration of the relationship between exercise and a healthy body will develop an understanding of processes such as breathing and circulation of the blood. Through a whole investigation on vision and eyesight, the children will be using different variables and carrying out a fair test. The range of starting points for this particular topic is endless.

BACKGROUND

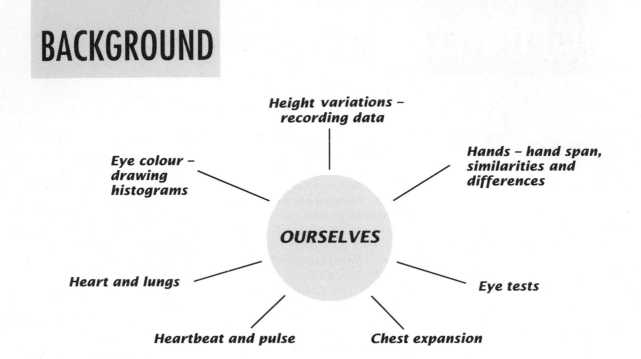

Height variations – recording data

Eye colour – drawing histograms

Hands – hand span, similarities and differences

OURSELVES

Heart and lungs

Eye tests

Heartbeat and pulse

Chest expansion

Activity	AT1	Statement of Attainment
1. Hands	1a 2a 2b 2c	– Observe – Question – Observe – Conclude
2. Colour it blue	PoS 2b	– Record data – Make related observations
3. Walking tall	PoS 3a 3b	– Record data – Question – Measure
4. Chest expansion	4b 4c	– Carry out a fair test – Measure volume – Detect patterns
5. Taking exercise – heartbeat	4a 4b 4c	– Question, predict – Carry out a fair test – Measure time intervals – Conclude – Link results to questions
6. Taking exercise – aerobics	5a 5b 5c	– Hypothesise – Consider variables – Interpret
7. Whole investigation – testing eyesight	Level 3	

ACTIVITIES

1. Hands

Age range
Key Stage 1.

Group size
Individuals, pairs, whole class.

What you need
Paper, pencils, crayons, large jar or tin holding a collection of marbles of the same size, smaller tin to collect the marbles in.

What to do
This activity can be introduced through a class discussion by drawing on children's natural curiosity about themselves.

First ask the children to look at their own hands and then compare them with a partner's hands. How are they the same? How are they different? Ask them to look closely – are there any lines on their hands?

Encourage them to ask questions such as the following:
• What shape are their nails?
• Can they see the half-moon shape on their nails?
• Which of the two children has the bigger hands?
• Is their right hand bigger than the left?

The children can work with a partner again and draw round each other's hands on a large sheet of paper. Help them to cut out their 'paper hands'.

The children can go on to compare their hand spans. Find the smallest and largest hand spans in the class.

They can investigate how many marbles they can pick out of a large tin. First they should try using their right hand and then their left. Can they hold more marbles with one hand than the other? Make sure you have a smaller tin available so that the children can transfer their marbles to it for counting. The results of these investigations can be written on a chart next to a display of the children's 'paper hands'. (Make sure the children write their names on their paper hands so that they can identify them.) Ask them to compare their results with their predictions.

Investigative skills
The children have looked closely at their own hands. They have asked questions such as 'Are my hands bigger than my partner's?' They have made related observations in comparing hand spans and they have drawn conclusions.

Content

The children will find similarities and differences between themselves when they carry out this investigation. There will be a wide variation in hand span and the number of marbles that are picked out of the tin by each child.

Further activity

This activity could lead on to an investigation of the children's feet. Do the children with the smallest hands have the smallest feet? Investigate shoe size.

AT1/1a,2a,2b,2c;
AT2/1a PoS(ii)

2. Colour it blue

Age range

Key Stage 1 and 2.

Group size

Whole class.

What you need

Paper, pencils, squared paper, coloured pencils, rulers.

What to do

This activity can be introduced as part of a topic or discussion on differences and similarities in themselves. The children will be keen to discover facts about themselves resulting from the discussion on individual similarities and differences. As a class, ask them to carry out a survey on eye colour. It is useful to establish categories of eye colour before the survey is undertaken. (Is brownish-grey the same as greyish-brown? Identify the difference between hazel and brown eyes.) A class record can be made of the data collected. The children should then represent their results as a histogram by plotting the number of children against eye colour. Once the graph is drawn, it is important to discuss the results. Are there more children in the class with blue eyes? Which is the most unusual eye colour?

The children could go on to construct a family tree of eye colours. What colour eyes do their brother and sisters, parents and grandparents have? Can they find a pattern?

Investigative skills

The children have made a series of related observations – 'The colour of my eyes is blue, your eyes are brown'. They have collected their results and represented these results as a histogram.

Content

The children have investigated similarities and differences between themselves. Eye colour is an inherited characteristic. It is not affected by the environment, for example, you cannot change your eye colour by altering your diet.

Further activity

Other surveys such as hair colour or hair type (straight or curly or wavy) could be undertaken to illustrate other similarities and differences among the class members.

AT1/2b PoS; AT2 PoS(ii)

3. Walking tall

Age range

Key Stage 2.

Group size

Whole class.

What you need

Tape measure or metre rulers, squared paper, pencils, coloured pencils, rulers.

What to do

This activity can be introduced by talking to the children about the differences of height within the class. What do they think influences how tall or how small they are?

Ask the children to carry out a survey to measure the heights of the children in the class. An easy way is for them

to mark out a height scale in centimetres on a door or wall. The scale should be just higher than the tallest child in the class. They can ask questions such as 'Who is the tallest?' 'Who is the smallest?' 'What is the most common height in the class?' 'Do small children have small parents?'

The children should collect the data on a class record sheet and draw the results on a bar chart of number of children against height. This should be grouped into categories, for example, number of children with heights between 100cm and 109cm, number of children with heights between 110cm and 119cm and so on.

What does this chart look like? How many children are in each height group? Which height group includes the most children?

Investigative skills
The children have asked questions and made accurate measurements. They have systematically collected their data and recorded it on a bar chart.

Content
There are no distinct categories of height. People are not either tall or short. There are many possible intermediates between very short and very tall. The graph should show a normal distribution, that is, a larger number of the children's heights will be somewhere in the middle of the range of heights measured. Height is an inherited factor but will be influenced by environmental factors such as health and diet. A person may inherit genes for tallness and yet may not be able to get enough food to grow tall. The children will

recognise that there is a variation in height among themselves. These differences are mainly due to heredity, that is, genes inherited from their parents. There may be several pairs of genes which control height.

Further activity
The children could carry out a similar activity measuring weight.

AT1/3a,3b PoS;
AT2 PoS(ii)

4. Chest expansion

Age range
Key Stage 2.

Group size
Groups of four.

What you need
Large sweet jar or bell jar, sink, tape measure, a piece of rubber tubing, a permanent fibre tip pen, paper and pencil, 250 or 500cm³ measuring

cylinder or beaker. Alternatively, a lung volume bag kit (Philip Harris).

What to do
Get a large sweet jar or bell jar and calibrate its volume by pouring in 250cm³ or 500cm³ of water. Mark the level with the permanent marker, before adding another similar volume of water and repeating the marking. Continue until the jar is almost full. Empty the water, invert the jar and write the volumes, for example, 1,500cm³, against the appropriate mark and then fill the jar by placing it in the sink. (It is important that when one child is blowing into the rubber tube, the other should be holding the jar to make sure it remains vertical, as shown below.) The apparatus is now ready to measure the volume of the children's lungs (lung capacity).

Working in pairs, let the children take each other's chest measurement, and then take it again when they have breathed in deeply and to a maximum. The chest

Name	Chest size at rest (cm)	Chest size after breating in (cm)	Chest expansion (cm)

expansion may then be calculated and displayed in a table similar to that shown above. Alternatively, the children may devise their own table. Who has the biggest chest expansion? Do big people generally have a larger chest expansion than small people? Do good athletes have a larger chest expansion? Show the children the apparatus to measure the volume of their lungs. Demonstrate how it works by taking a deep breath while holding your nose, and then breathing out through the tube (without taking air in through the nose). The air you breath out forces water out of the container and this is approximately equivalent to the volume of your lungs. However, some air still remains in the lungs which may not be expelled. Instruct the children how to measure the volume accurately. Ask them to make predictions about people and lung capacity. They might suggest that 'boys will have a larger capacity than girls' or 'bigger people will have a larger lung capacity than smaller people'. Hopefully someone might suggest that 'people with a large chest expansion will have a large lung capacity'. Ask the children how they would investigate this and how they would make it a fair test. How would they record their results? (The table below may be helpful.) Ask them to look for patterns in their observations and to relate these to the original prediction or idea.

Investigative skills

You have helped the children to ask a question, suggest ideas and make predictions with the help of your prior knowledge. The children will probably have carried out a fair test and measured volume. However, the rigour of the fair test is not particularly great in this investigation. Some of the children might be able to detect that there is, (or is not), a pattern between lung capacity and chest expansion. Talk to the children about the lungs, lung capacity, chest expansion and athletic achievement.

Content

The lungs are the organs in the body which take in air and transfer oxygen into the blood. They also collect carbon dioxide from the blood and expel it from the body. The lungs are made up of thousands of little sacs called *alveoli* which are in contact with blood capillaries. The volume of air contained in the lungs is called the *lung capacity*.

The maximum amount of air that can be breathed out is called the *vital capacity*. The vital capacity of an average ten year-old boy and girl is $2000cm^3$ and $1800cm^3$ respectively. However, a further $1000cm^3$ still remains in the lungs (*residual volume*) and this needs to be added to give the lung capacity. During breathing while resting, only about $400cm^3$ is taken in and expelled. A relationship might be noted between chest expansion and lung capacity and possibly also the ability to be successful at certain sports. Breathing and respiration is one of the seven life processes common to all living things.

Safety

Children with respiratory problems would be advised not to carry out this activity or to breath in and out but not to maximum potential. Water should be kept away from electrical items and spillages should be mopped up immediately to avoid accidents.

AT1/4b,4c; AT2/3a,4a,5a

5. Taking exercise – heartbeat

Age range
Key Stage 2.

Group size
Pairs, small groups.

Name	Chest expansion (cm)	Water removed = volume of lungs

What you need

Stop-watch.

What to do

This activity can be introduced by a discussion on the importance of taking regular exercise to keep fit and healthy.

The children could talk about the sports they take part in and which they enjoy most. Ask them to think about what happens to their heartbeat during exercise.

What differences do the children notice after they have taken exercise? (They will identify that they get out of breath and that they feel hot and their faces become flushed.)

Explain to the children that the heart rate can be measured by taking the pulse either in their wrist or in their neck. You will need to demonstrate how this is done. The children can design and carry out an investigation to see how exercise affects heart rate and how quickly they recover after exercise. They may hypothesise, 'The higher the pulse rate during exercise, the longer the recovery period.' They should make sure they design a fair test to compare recovery rates of their group or whole class.

This investigation will involve the children in using a stop-watch and recording pulse rate (number of beats per minute) before exercise, immediately after exercise, and at regular intervals after exercise until the pulse rate returns to its normal rate. The children should make a record of their results. They could draw a bar chart of the pulse rate before, during and after the exercise. The recovery rates of the whole class can be compared by comparing the results and the graphs. Is the fittest child in the class the child with the fastest recovery rate?

Investigative skills

The children have made predictions based on prior knowledge (effect of exercise on their bodies) and have carried out a fair test. They have quantified their results using a timer. They have drawn conclusions based on their results. They have represented their results in graphical form.

Content

Taking regular exercise is beneficial to our health. Muscles are strengthened, the efficiency of the heart and lungs is increased and it helps to control our weight. When we take exercise our heart beats faster, our pulse rate increases and we breathe at a faster rate. After exercise, a fit person would recover more quickly than someone who never took exercise.

Safety

It may not be advisable for children with respiratory problems to take part in this investigation.

AT1/4a, 4b, 4c; AT2/5a PoS(i)

6. Taking exercise – aerobics

Age range
Key Stage 2.

Group size
Individuals, small groups.

What you need
Stop-watch, paper, pencils.

What to do
This activity can be introduced through discussion of 'how we keep fit'. Ask the children about different forms of exercise which the family take. This could naturally lead in to discussion about aerobics classes. This activity is appropriate to be undertaken after the children have completed the investigation on heart rate.

Ask the children to list changes which occur in their bodies after exercise. The children will include in this list the fact that their breathing rates increase. This is one of the effects of taking part in aerobics. The children will have already learned through the previous investigation on heart beat that their hearts beat faster during exercise in order to pump blood round the body at a faster rate, thus pumping more oxygen to the muscles. Using this acquired knowledge the following investigation can be undertaken. This new investigation now sets out to explore the relationship between breathing rate and heart rate.

The children can try measuring their breathing rates while they are sitting quietly at their desks. They can count the number of times they breathe in over a period of one minute. Encourage them to think about fair testing and accuracy – they could repeat the test and take an average of the two results.

Ask the children to design an investigation to predict and then measure their breathing rates when doing different activities, for example, walking, running, jumping up and down, skipping.

They could discuss and predict the number of breaths they would take each minute if they were sleeping – is it going to be more or less than during some of the above activities?

They could measure their heart rate (by measuring their pulse rate) before and after some of these activities. The children can record their results on a bar chart to show the number of breaths taken each minute during the different activities. They might also wish to draw a graph showing pulse rate after each of the activities. The graphs showing breathing rate and heart rate can then be compared. Class results can also be compared.

Investigative skills
The children will have formulated hypotheses such as 'The breathing rate and heart rate are related. When one increases so does the other'. They will know that more oxygen will need to be supplied to the muscles during exercise.

They have carried out fair tests and recorded their results systematically. They have then gone on to represent these results in graphical form and compared their results with those of other class members.

Content
When we take part in aerobics or other exercise, we need more oxygen from the air and we need to take more air into our lungs. The oxygen passes out of our lungs into our blood. The heart pumps this 'oxygenated' blood round our bodies to the cells in our body. The heart beats faster and pumps blood to our cells at a faster rate in order to supply the muscle cells with more oxygen when it is needed. As more oxygen is needed during exercise both heart rates and breathing rates increase.

Safety
It may not be advisable for children with respiratory problems to take part in this investigation.

AT1/5a,5b,5c; AT2/5a PoS(i)

7. Whole investigation – testing eyesight

Age range
Key Stage 1 and 2.

Group size
Pairs or small groups.

What you need
Metre rulers, large pieces of paper, pencils, felt pens.

What to do
How do I introduce the investigation?
This investigation can be introduced through discussion about our eyes and that some people wear spectacles to help them to see more clearly. The children will probably know of a friend or a relative who wears spectacles for reading, or other people who wear spectacles to help them see objects at a distance.

What questions might the children ask?
Encourage the children to ask questions such as 'How far can I see?' or 'Do both my eyes work as well as each other?', 'Which coloured object can I see better at a distance?'
(AT1/3a)

What observations might the children make?
The children could make preliminary tests by going outside into the playground in pairs and seeing how far away they can stand from each other and still be able to read a book or a poster. They could test out the distances they have to stand from each other when they can still distinguish one coloured object from another.
(AT1/3b)

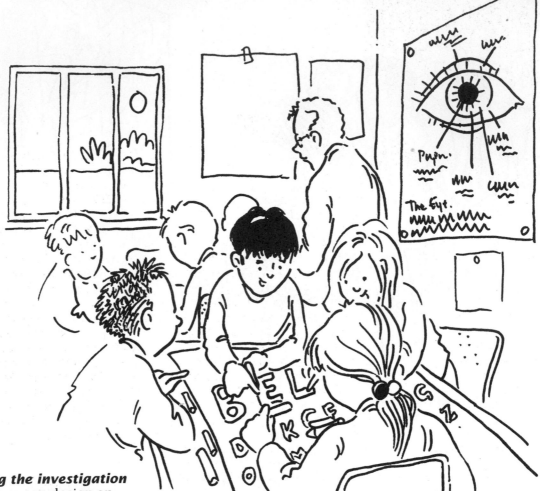

Designing the investigation

The children can design an investigation to see how far they can see or who can see the most letters on an eye chart at a fixed distance. They could test to see if both their eyes work equally as well. They could work in groups and design an eye test chart either by drawing letters or shapes in decreasing size. How can they make it a fair test? They should consider what they will need to measure and how they will make their measurements. How will they record their results? Will they test both eyes together or the right and left eyes separately?

They could develop the investigation further by trying to identify if we see some colours more easily than others at a distance. They could use different coloured letters of the same size on a chart. *(AT1/3b,3c)*

How will the children record their findings?

The children can make a group recording sheet which will include how they carried out their investigation and the results they obtained.

Interpreting the results

Encourage the children to discuss their results and compare the designs of the investigation by different groups. They could consider how they might improve their tests. They will be able to draw conclusions and realise that some children can see further than others. *(AT1/3d)*

What else might the children investigate?

The children could test their range of vision or they could design eyesight tests using letters on different coloured backgrounds. Does the background colour make a difference to how easily the letters are read? *(AT1/3c)*

Content

There is a lens in the eye which focuses images on the sensitive area in the eye. This is called the retina. Some people need spectacles because the lens in the eye is not working properly.
(KS1 AT2, PoS(i)
KS2 AT2/3a PoS(ii))

CHAPTER 13

Earth and space

Human beings have always had a fascination for the Moon, Sun, stars and planets, and this has been reflected in the civilisations of the ancient Greeks and the Egyptians. Later, Copernicus and Galileo added to knowledge and understanding of the universe. More recently, the USA and the former Soviet Union have spent large amounts of money in the 'Space Race' and on space research and exploration.

While it may be considered that the topic of Earth and Space does not offer a rich area for children's practical investigation, there are still opportunities for such activities. Young children may investigate some characteristics of the season such as the weather, hours of daylight, what they might wear and changes to the trees. They might also be able to track the apparent movement of the Sun across the sky, if the clouds stay away long enough! Close observation of pictures of the Sun, Earth and Moon will aid their understanding that these are separate bodies in space.

At a later age, children may investigate the phases of the Moon and be able to predict what the Moon will look like in a day or two's time, clouds again permitting! Some children are fascinated by the planets whose relative positions and distances from the Sun may be investigated with reference to home-made or commercial models. Investigation with sun-dials will help to develop children's understanding of shadows and the postition and angle of the Sun in the sky, at various times of the day. Finally, a whole investigation at levels 3 and 4 helps children to investigate and understand why we have night and day.

BACKGROUND

Seasonal changes
- length of daylight
- weather and the seasons
- changes in plants – flowering
  – leaf fall
- changes in animals – migration

**Earth, Sun and Moon –
separate bodies in space**
- the motions which explain day and night, day length, phases of the Moon, and the seasons

EARTH AND SPACE

The Sun
- tracking its path; shadow stick or sun-dial

The Moon
- phases of the moon
- the night sky

Planets
- position and appearance of bright planets
- order and movement around the sun
- distances from the sun

Activity	AT1	Statement of Attainment
1. Seasonal changes	1a, 2b	– Observe
2. Apparent movement of the Sun	1a, 2b 2a 2c	– Observe – Question, predict – Interpret results
3. What's their shape?	1a, 2b	– Observe
4. Phases of the Moon	2b 3a 3d	– Observe – Question and predict – Interpret results
5. How far away?	3b	– Observe and measure
6. The angle of the Sun	3a, 4a 3b 3c, 3d, 4c	– Question and predict – Measure and manipulate variables – Interpret results
7. Whole investigation – night and day	Levels 3 and 4	

ACTIVITIES

1. Seasonal changes

Age range
Key Stage 1.

Group size
Small groups.

What you need
A Seasons Diary, newspapers, photocopiable page 186.

What to do
Provide the children with a Seasons Diary which they will keep over a period of time. It might be useful to start this activity in September when the summer holidays are still fresh in the children's minds and the last traces of that season are still with us. Get them to keep records in picture or written form of the following.
• the temperature – is it hot, cool or cold?
• the leaves on the trees – what colour are they?
• the swallows, swifts and martins – are they to be seen?
• the length of daylight – is it long or short?
• what the children wear outdoors – warm or cool clothing?
• what they do or cannot do – why is this?
Hours of daylight could be obtained from the newspapers or a diary, by direct observation or by parental help.
Give the children photocopiable page 186 and ask them to draw their observations on the partly completed pictures.
Discuss the findings with the whole class, highlighting the differences between the seasons.

Investigative skills
The children have observed events throughout the year and, by keeping a diary of the seasonal changes, have had the opportunity to make a series of related observations. These might include the length of the day or the changes taking place to the trees during the autumn term.

Content
The seasons are characterised by the different number of hours of daylight and different types of weather which bring about changes to plants and animals. In the Northern Hemisphere the hours of daylight are shortest in the winter and longest in the summer. The order of the seasons (winter, spring, summer and autumn) is constant. The teacher should be aware that the Earth takes 365.25 days to complete an orbit of the Sun. The Earth's axis is tilted at 23.5^0 from the vertical. Therefore, the North and South poles lean towards the Sun at different times of the year. When the South Pole is tilted towards the Sun in December, the Northern hemisphere has winter. Six months later in June, when the North Pole is tilted towards the Sun, the Southern Hemisphere is in the middle of winter. Thus the seasons are caused by the Earth's axis combined with its orbit around the Sun (see Figure 1 below).

AT1/1a,2b; AT4 PoS(v)

Figure 1

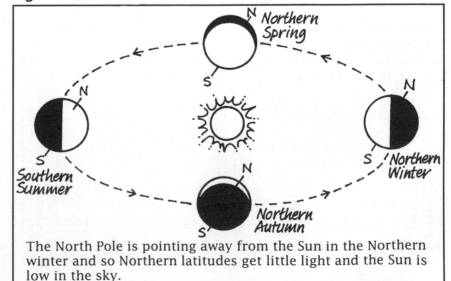

The North Pole is pointing away from the Sun in the Northern winter and so Northern latitudes get little light and the Sun is low in the sky.

2. Apparent movement of the Sun

Age range
Key Stage 1 and 2.

Group size
Small groups.

What you need
A window through which the sun may be observed for as much of the day as possible.

What to do
On a day when little or no thick cloud is expected, talk to the children about night and day. What causes the night? What is always present during the day, even if sometimes we cannot see it because it is behind the clouds? Ask the children if they have noticed any changes to the Sun during the day. Is it the same height in the sky? Does it appear to move in the sky? How does it appear to move?

Ask the children to draw accurate pictures looking out of the window at three or five times in the day to show the position of the Sun (see Safety section). Alternatively, you might like to provide them with a pre-drawn picture on to which they can add the Sun and times of the day, for example, early morning or 09.00.

Investigative skills
The children will have observed the apparent movement of the Sun and will have been given the opportunity to make a series of observations of the Sun's position during the day. Some of the children might have asked 'How does the Sun move?' or 'Why does it move?' and some might have offered ideas and predictions. When the pictures have been drawn, some of the children will be able to describe the 'rising and falling' of the Sun in the sky and compare this with their prediction.

Content
Children will have been given the opportunity over a period of time to observe the position of the Sun at a fixed time such as 09.00, 12.00 and 15.00. They will also have studied the apparent movement of the Sun across the sky during a whole day.

Further activity
The length of day could be discussed at different times of the year and the 'Sun pictures' (see Figure 1) could be repeated in both the summer and winter. In the winter, children will be aware that they wake up/come to school in the dark/dusk and in the summer that it is light in the morning (it may even wake them up) and light until late at night (difficult to go to sleep).

Safety
Direct observation of the Sun for even a short period of time will cause discomfort and blurring of vision. Prolonged viewing of the Sun is dangerous and must be avoided. For this reason it may be advisable to produce pre-drawn pictures of the view from out of the school window to reduce the viewing time.

AT1/1a,2a,2b,2c; AT4/1d

3. What's their shape?

Age range
Key Stage 1 and 2.

Group size
Small groups.

What you need
Pictures of the Sun and the Moon (Figure 2); pictures of the Earth from space; models of the solar system, mobiles which show spherical shapes, globe of the Earth, Plasticine.

What to do
Get the children to observe the variety of resources available to them. Ask them to share their findings in a group. What shape is the Sun, the Earth and the Moon? Which is the

Figure 1

Figure 2

biggest? Are they joined or are they separate? What are the differences between them? What are they surrounded by?

Ask the children to make Plasticine models of the Sun, Moon and the Earth.

Investigative skills
The children will have observed closely and made a series of observations of bodies in space.

Content
By observing the Moon and the Sun in an indirect way the children will become aware that they are separate bodies in space. This will be backed up by photographs and videos of the Moon and Earth from space which show that these bodies are spherical (ball shaped) as opposed to round. An idea of the spherical shape of the Moon may be gained by observing it through binoculars.

The Sun is a star, while the Earth is a planet. The Moon is a natural satellite of the Earth. The Earth orbits the Sun and the Moon orbits the Earth. The Earth revolves on its axis, thus giving night and day. The Moon revolves around the Earth but at such a speed that the same side always faces the Earth.

Safety
Children should not look directly at the Sun as it can damage their eyesight.

AT1/1a,2b; AT4/2e

4. Phases of the Moon

Age range
Key Stage 1 and 2.

Group size
Whole class, then small groups.

What you need
Photocopiable pages 187 and 188, chalk board or large piece of paper.

What to do
Talk to the children about the night sky. Ask them what they have seen. What shape is the Moon? Ask them to draw it on the board or a large piece of paper. Has anyone seen the Moon shaped differently? Give the children photocopiable page 187. Explain that the pictures on days 15 and 45 represent the Full Moon and the dotted pictures on days 1, 30 and 60 represent the New Moon. Ask them to use their knowledge and their diagrams of the Moon to predict what the other pictures will look like. Remind them that there will only be a small change from day to day. When they have completed this ask them why the Moon shines? Is it burning like the Sun?

Give them a copy of photocopiable sheet 188 and ask them to record the shape of the Moon each night, reminding them that they will not see the Moon on a cloudy night. Monitor their progress and inform them of the night of the New Moon when little or nothing will be visible.

Discuss the results and explore the patterns. Compare the predictions with the findings. If the children do not

Figure 3

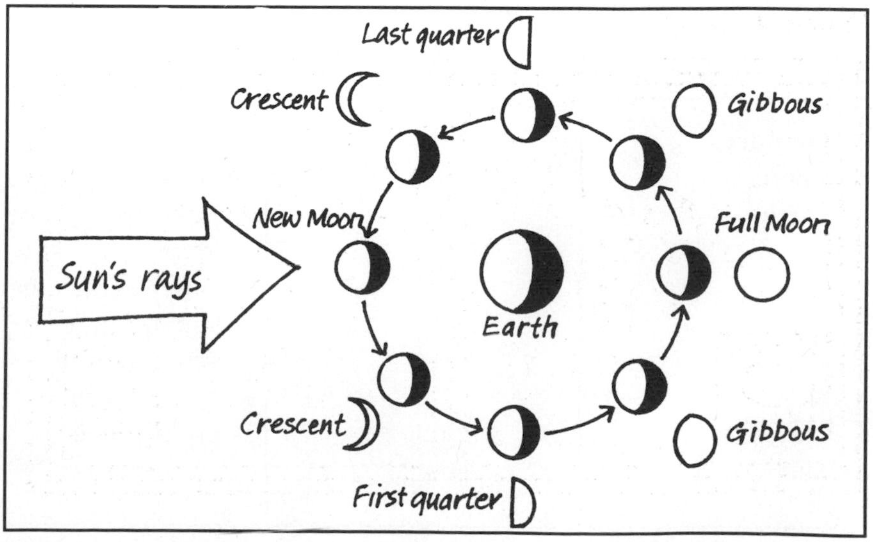

ask why there are different shapes, inform them that the Sun shines on the Moon which moves around the Earth. At different times we can see different amounts of the lit-up part of the Moon and that this gives the apparently different shapes (phases) of the Moon (see Figure 3 on the previous page).

Investigative skills

The children will have made a series of related observations if they carry out the 'Moon watch'.

Some children may have predicted the shapes (phases) of the Moon and verified these by observation. Some children may be able to describe what they have seen and explain the different shapes of the Moon.

Content

The children will have observed the position of the Moon in the sky (day and night) and will have been aware of its apparent change in shape. They should be aware that a New Moon is present every 30 days (actually 29.5 days) and that the Full Moon is present 15 days after the New Moon. They should know the order of the phases of the Moon. They could also be introduced to the terms crescent, first quarter, gibbous and last quarter to describe the shape of the Moon. The children should be made aware that unlike the Sun, the Moon does not produce its own light (it is not a light source) but is lit up because the light from the Sun is reflected off its surface.

AT1/2b,3a,3d; AT4/3d,3e

5. How far away?

Age range
Key Stage 1 and 2.

Group size
Pairs.

What you need
A table or bench (6m in length) on which the planets and the Sun are attached in the appropriate places. These could be represented by seeds or balls of proportionate size (see diagram opposite) labelled with the names of planets.

What to do
Ask the children what they know about the solar system, explaining that the Earth is one of the nine planets in that system. Remind the children through questioning that the Sun is a star and is similar to the other stars in the sky but is much closer to us.

Draw and colour in a small portion of the Sun, ensuring that it is very much larger than any of the planets. Place this at the end of the bench or floor. Space out the planets on the bench/floor, so that they are 1mm away from the Sun for every million km distance they are actually away from it (see the diagram at the top of the next page). For example, Mercury would be 58mm from the edge of the Sun and Pluto would be 5,940mm.

Ask the children to measure the distances from the Sun to each planet, pointing out that

Planet/Star	Approximate diameter in relation to the Earth (cm)	Represented by	Distance from the sun (million km)
Mercury	0.4	Poppy seed	58
Venus	1.0	dried pea/peppercorn	108
Earth	1.0	dried pea/peppercorn	150
Mars	0.5	lentil	228
Jupiter	11.0	super bounce ball	778
Saturn	9.5	super bounce ball	1427
Uranus	3.7	small marble	2870
Neptune	3.5	small marble	4497
Pluto	0.5	poppy seed	5940
Sun	109.0		

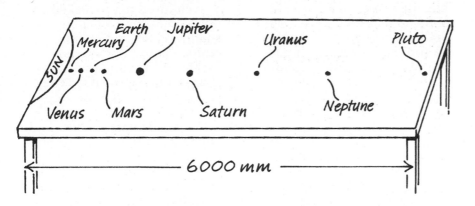

Earth Jupiter
Mercury Uranus Pluto
SUN
Venus Mars Saturn Neptune

⟵ 6000 mm ⟶

the real distance can be found by multiplying their answer in millimetres by a million kilometres.

Investigative skills
The children will have measured the distances from the planets to the Sun.

Ensure that the children know that planets orbit the Sun. (You could explain, however, that early scientists thought that the Earth was the centre of the whole universe and that the Sun and all the other planets orbited the Earth.)

Content
Children should study the appearance and position of the planets and know about the order and orbits of the planets around the Sun.

The children should be made aware that the orbits of the planets are not circular but elliptical and hence the distance from the Sun varies.

AT1/3b; AT4 PoS(v)

Further activity
Make Plasticine models of the planets, carry out movement activities to represent their order and orbits and look at videos to try to make the concept of the planets and their orbits more concrete.

6. The angle of the Sun

Age range
Key Stage 1 and 2.

Group size
Small groups.

What you need
Various objects to produce shadows, the school yard and chalk or a large piece of paper and a pen, a variety of sticks, plant pot or plastic bottle containing soil.

What to do
On a sunny day give the children a variety of objects and ask them to investigate shadows. How can they make

their own shadow smaller? Will a large or a small stick produce a larger shadow? Do shadows remain the same size throughout the day?

Encourage the children to make some suggestions and predictions about the size of shadows throughout the day. If they are unable to do this suggest an hypothesis such as 'The size of the shadow will change as the Sun rises and falls in the sky.' and write this on the board.

Ask the children how they might test the(ir) idea and prediction. Ask them to carry out a fair test, record their results and take some measurements. Is it important, or would it be useful to record the time? How many readings are they going to take; one every minute/ten minutes/half an hour/hour? Tell them to draw a simple diagram (like the one below) of the position of the Sun in the sky and to record the time, ensuring that they are aware of the dangers of looking at the Sun.

After they have carried out their investigation (hopefully the Sun has continued to shine), ask them whether they have carried out a fair test. Get them to display their results. Was there a pattern to their

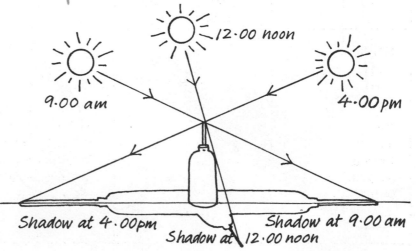

12.00 noon

9.00 am 4.00 pm

Shadow at 4.00pm Shadow at 9.00 am
Shadow at 12.00 noon

results? Ask the children to explain why shorter shadows were obtained near the middle of the day.

Investigative skills

Some of the children might have made a prediction such as 'The size of the shadows will be long in the morning and afternoon, but small at midday' or 'The size of the shadow will change as the Sun rises and falls in the sky; it will be small at midday but longer in the morning and afternoon' and then proceed to suggest ideas on how to set about showing this.

The children should have the opportunity to carry out a fair test, for example, by placing a stick in a bottle of soil and measuring the length (and position) of the shadow so formed. The stick should not be moved during the day. It should be noted that the rigour of setting up and maintaining a fair test is not very demanding in this investigation.

The children might have been able to explain how they had set up a fair test and to say that the position of the Sun was responsible for the differences in shadow length. Others might have been able to interpret the pattern of their results by explaining that the low angle of the Sun in the morning and afternoon produces a long shadow, while the high angle of the Sun at midday produces a short shadow.

Content

The children have tracked the position of the Sun using a shadow clock and should realise that the position and height of the Sun appears to change during the day. They should realise that this principle is used in the sun-dial. They should be encouraged to appreciate that the angle of the Sun determines the size of the shadow so produced. In the morning and at the end of the day the Sun is low in the sky and this low angle produces a large shadow. Conversely, in the middle of the day when the Sun is at its maximum height, the shadow is smaller, as is seen in the diagram at the bottom of the previous page.

Safety

Direct observation of the Sun for even a short period of time will cause discomfort and blurring of vision. Prolonged viewing of the Sun is dangerous and must be avoided.

AT1/3a,3b,3c,3d,4a,4c; AT4/2d,3e

7. Whole investigation – night and day

Age range
Key Stage 2.

Group size
Small groups.

What you need
Room with blackouts, overhead projector, slide projector or very bright, strong torch, globe.

What to do
How do I introduce the investigation?
Ask the children questions about the Earth and the Sun to refresh their memories about the relative positions in the solar system and the movement of the Earth around the Sun. Ask them, drawing on previous work, why we have night and day and why the day length varies during the year (seasons).

Ask the children to ask a question or make a prediction or hypothesis, verify it by investigation using equipment of their choice and record and interpret their findings.

What questions might the children ask and what predictions might they make?
Children working at level 4 will be able to predict that night and day are due to the Sun shining on the Earth, while those at Level 5 will be able to relate this to the Earth revolving around the Sun.

Children working at level 4a will be able to predict that the differences in day length and the seasons are caused by the angle of the Sun, while those at Level 5a will be able to

Figure 1

relate this to the Earth's axis and elliptical orbit. **(AT1/ 4a,5a)** The latter children will formulate a hypothesis such as 'The day length will be shorter in the winter in the UK because the North Pole (hemisphere) is tilted away from the Sun, where it will receive less hours of sunlight'.

What observations might the children make?
The children will be able to see that while it is light in the United Kingdom it is dark in Australia. With a bright light source and using a globe, the children will be able to see that as the Earth orbits the Sun the time the United Kingdom is light will vary, particularly if a shadow clock is used (see Figures 1 and 2).

Designing the investigation, variables involved, fair testing, testing the hypothesis
The children should be aware that day length is the variable to be measured, that the variable to be changed is the position of the Earth on its orbit and that the position of

the light source should remain constant, though not necessarily the distance from the Earth. They should consider how to measure the differences they find. **(AT1/ 3b,4b)**

How will the children record their findings?
Recording is difficult but could include:
• use of shadow clocks to record the time the Sun rises and sets in the UK at different times of the year;
• measuring the 'length' of light at the same longitude as the UK at different times of the year;
• rotating the globe at a constant speed and recording the time it takes from sunrise to sunset over the UK at different times of the year.

Interpreting results
Some children might be able to link their observations to their original prediction, by commenting on the presence of day and night in different parts of the globe/world **(AT1/3c)**, while others will be able to relate this to the

revolving Earth. *(AT1/4c)*
What else might the children investigate?
The children could investigate the differences in time in different capitals of the world, using their shadow clocks, and compare them with published time differences. Adjustments might have to be made for British Summer Time.

Content

The Earth (a planet) orbits the Sun (a star) revolving anticlockwise at it does so. It revolves once every 24 hours. When one side of the Earth has daytime the other side has night because the Sun's rays are not shining on it.

The seasons and day length are attributable to the position of the Earth's axis. The Earth's

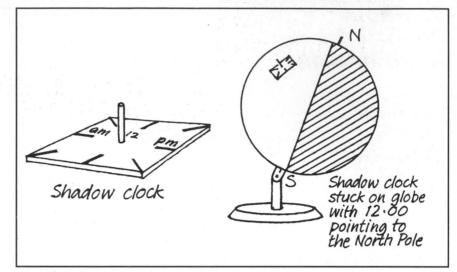

Figure 2

orbit is elliptical with the North/South axis on a tilt 23.5° from the vertical. The Earth spins around this axis but during its orbit around the Sun the 'tilt' remains the same. Thus, the direction in which the poles point remain the same all the way around the Sun. This produces our seasons and the changes in

day length. In the Northern Winter, the North Pole is pointing away from the Sun and therefore northern latitudes get little light and the Sun is low in the sky. In the Northern Summer, the North Pole is pointing towards the Sun and therefore northern latitudes get much light and the Sun is much higher in the sky.

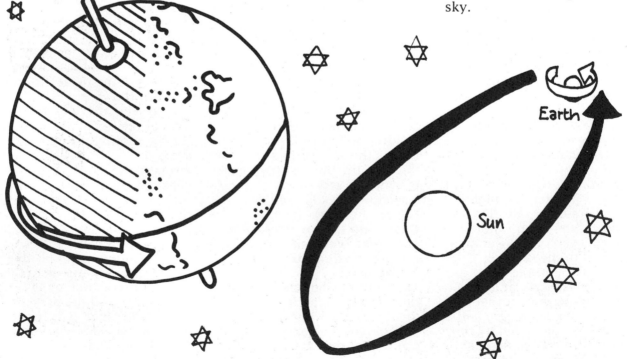

CHAPTER 14

Science in the kitchen

The familiar environment of the kitchen provides an ideal context for scientific investigations. Children need to be aware of important issues such as food preservation, hygiene and safe handling of food. Many of the activities in the kitchen such as cooking, mixing, washing and food preparation have a scientific basis which children will enjoy exploring. With such a wide range of investigations to choose from, you may well be spoilt for choice. This chapter focuses on a number of investigations to illustrate this breadth of choice.

Observation of frozen foods is a good way to start. Children can then investigate materials using everyday kitchen equipment. A visit to the local supermarket can be the starting point for a comparison of different types of washing powder or an investigation into the strengths of different types of flour. A whole investigation into the conditions needed for the growth of yeast emphasises the importance of fair testing and consideration of variables. Science in the kitchen provides opportunities for encouraging children to plan and carry out explorations and develop important investigative skills.

BACKGROUND

Materials in the kitchen
- metals, non-metals
- insulating materials
- absorbency
- packaging
- detergents

Food and drink
- waste food
- bread and flours, yeast
- changes in food – chemical and physical
- frozen food

SCIENCE IN THE KITCHEN

Safety and hygiene
- safe handling of food
- keeping food cool

Machines/equipment
- electricity
- sieving
- whisking (gears)
- timers

Activity	AT1	Statement of Attainment
1. Freezing up	1a 2a 2b	– Observe familiar materials – Predict – Observe
2. Kitchen equipment	3a	– Predict
3. Flour – how strong is it?	3a 3b	– Question, predict – Observe
4. Material thoughts	3a 4b	– Question, predict – Carry out a fair test
5. Wash day	4a 4b	– Question, predict – Carry out a fair test
6. Hard or soft?	2b 4a 4b	– Observe – Question, predict – Carry out a fair test
7. Whole investigation – the conditions yeast needs to grow	Level 5	

ACTIVITIES

1. Freezing up

Age range
Key Stage 1.

Group size
Small groups.

What you need
A range of frozen foods, for example: vegetables, fish fingers, chips, ice cream. Trays, weighing scales, stop clock.

What to do
Discuss with the children the reasons for keeping food in freezers. Why do we need freezers? When would we put food in a freezer rather than in a fridge? Is all the food that we put in the freezer already frozen or can we put fresh food into a freezer? Ask the children to talk about the different foods that might be found in a freezer at home. Show them the frozen foods that are available for this investigation. There are some markings on the labels of all of these foods. What do they mean? How long can we store food in a freezer?

The children can carry out an investigation using the frozen foods available. If possible, make available similar defrosted foods for comparisons. They could make detailed observations of individual items of food as they defrost. Does the food look the same frozen and defrosted? Encourage them to record the changes they observe in the food. They could weigh the food frozen and defrosted. Is there a difference? Can they see moisture present as the foods defrost? If so, where has it come from? Is there a change in texture? Does a fish finger defrost more quickly or slowly than a pea or piece of sweet corn? If so, why? How does ice cream look different when it is not frozen. What happens to ice cream if you leave it for a long time or put it in a warm place? Can you re-freeze the foods? Do they look the same after re-freezing? Is there one part of the freezer which is colder than the rest?

The children could make a chart recording their results and talk to the rest of the class about their findings.

Investigative skills
The children have observed familiar materials and events. They have asked questions, suggested ideas and made predictions. They have also made a series of related observations.

Content

Domestic freezers maintain a temperature of approximately –18°C. Freezers can be used to freeze fresh food and to store pre-frozen food whereas refrigerators can only store fresh food. Food freezers and refrigerators are marked with a 'star' coding which gives guidance about freezing:

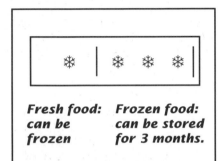

Fresh food: can be frozen **Frozen food: can be stored for 3 months.**

The stars in the right-hand box indicate the frozen food storage time. One star means frozen food can be stored up to one week, two stars indicate frozen food can be stored up to one month, and three stars mean that frozen food can be stored for up to three months.

The storage life of frozen food depends on the star marking of the refrigerator or freezer.

When food freezes there will also be formation of ice crystals (from the water in the food, on the surface of the food, or in the atmosphere).

AT1/1a,2a,2b; AT4 PoS(ii)

2. Kitchen equipment

Age range
Key Stage 1 and 2.

Group size
Pairs or small groups.

What you need
Catalogues, magazines, scissors, adhesive, pencils, paper, hot water, metal and wooden spoons.

What to do
Kitchen utensils and equipment are made of a variety of different materials. This activity links the properties of the material to its everyday use in the kitchen.

Discuss with the children the range of utensils and equipment used in the kitchen every day. Ask the children to make a list of some of these items which they have in their own kitchens at home. These would include saucepans, cutlery, food containers, cooking utensils such as spoons, knives, chopping board, baking tins, washing-up bowls, buckets and so on. Encourage the children to consider what material each item is made from and why they think that particular material is most suitable for the item, for example, wooden handles on saucepans for insulating, metal saucepans – good conductors of electricity, plastic – possible to mould and shape for different size containers and to store strong smelling foods. The children could devise a recording sheet which would include the item/ utensil, the material it is made of and its use within the kitchen. Once back in the classroom ask the children to search through the catalogues for pictures of kitchen utensils. They can cut these out and make a chart dividing the items into sets depending upon the material from which it is made. Some items may be made of more than one material, for example, metal

saucepan with a wooden handle – a Venn diagram could be constructed illustrating the common features of these utensils. Which materials are natural and which are man-made?

The children could compare metal and wooden spoons to find out which are insulators and which are conductors. Great care needs to be taken here. This can be done by standing wooden and metal spoons in bowls of cold and warm water with their handles sticking out and testing after a few minutes to see if one is warmer than the other. The children could also test how effective plastic containers are at containing smells from strong-smelling foods, for example, an onion or ripe cheese.

Investigative skills
The children have investigated a range of materials and suggested ideas and predictions relating properties to use.

Content
Materials can be natural (wood) or man-made (plastic and stainless steel). This activity helps the children to understand that materials have different properties (conductors or insulators of

heat can be moulded and have high melting points). These properties are related to the use of the material. Heat travels very slowly along a wooden spoon – it is a good insulator (a poor conductor). Metal has a high conductivity and will heat up quickly.

AT1/3a; AT3/2a,3a

3. Flour – how strong is it?

Age range
Key Stage 1 and 2.

Group size
Small groups.

What you need
Samples of different types of flour, hand lenses, sieves of varying mesh, paper, pencils, water, weighing scales, measuring cylinder, mixing bowl, rulers.

What to do
The children could visit the local supermarket to see the range of flours that are on sale. (If there is a bakery there, they may be able to visit it.)

Ask the children whether they prefer white or brown bread. Discuss why bread is brown or white and relate this to the different types of flour. Is one type of bread healthier to eat than another? The children can then make detailed observations of the samples of flour. They can compare the colour and texture. What do they notice when they sieve the flours? – they can use sieves of varying mesh. What is left behind in the sieve? Is there anything left behind when the white flour is sieved?

Flours used for bread-making often say 'strong' flour on the packet. Ask the children what they think this means. Can they test the 'strength' of a flour? Ask them to compare different flour strengths. They can predict which flour they think will produce the strongest dough and go on to make up different doughs by adding 75cm^3 of water to 120gm flour. Use plain white flour, 'strong' white flour recommended for bread-making, wholemeal flour and brown flour. When the doughs

are mixed, the children should roll each one into a sausage shape 10cm long. They should pull each end of the dough to see how far it will stretch before breaking. The results can be recorded on a chart showing type of flour and length before breaking. Small samples of each type of flour could be put into a polythene bag and the bag stapled on to the chart.

Investigative skills
The children have made close observations, asked questions and made predictions.

Content
When wholemeal flour is sieved, the brown flakes which areleft in the sieve (the bran) come from the outer skin of wheat seed. Most of the wheat germ is also trapped in the sieve.

When flour is mixed with water it becomes sticky like glue because of a protein in the flour called gluten. Gluten is important in bread-making for retaining the carbon dioxide produced by the yeast and for maintaining the structure of the bread. The stretchability of the dough depends on the amount of gluten present. Flours with relatively high gluten content are described as being 'strong' and these are used in bread-making.

AT1/3a,3b; AT3/2a,4a

4. Material thoughts

Age range
Key Stage 2.

Group size
Small groups.

What you need
A dropper, 6 transparent plastic cups, 6 samples of different kitchen cloths, elastic bands.

What to do
There are a wide range of kitchen cloths on the market for mopping up spills. This investigation compares the absorbency of these materials.

Discuss with the children how they might compare the absorbency of the kitchen cloths provided. They could predict which of the cloths they think will absorb most water. They may make hypotheses such as, 'The thickest cloth will soak up the most water.' They need to consider the variables involved and to ensure that they carry out a 'fair test'. How will they measure absorbency? What will they need to keep the same? They will need to consider factors such as the size of fabric to be tested and the amount of water used in each test. The cloth samples could be tested in a number of ways. They could be fastened over the plastic cups and secured with the elastic bands. The water could be dropped in single drops on top of the cloths. Does the drop of water remain on top of the cloth? How many drops will each cloth absorb before water starts dropping into the cups?

Alternatively, strips of cloth could be cut and suspended into the cups containing equal amounts of water. Amounts of water left in the cups could be measured after timed intervals. Again, how can the children ensure a 'fair test'? How else could they measure absorbency – for example, the height to which the dampness extends or length of time for water to soak up to a marked height?

It is important for the children to consider how they will record their results. They could stick samples of the kitchen cloths next to their results to make a collage.

Investigative skills
The children have made predictions as to which is the most absorbent kitchen cloth.

They have carried out a fair test and considered the variables involved.

Content
The children will discover that the kitchen cloths vary in the amount of water they have absorbed. They could relate this property to the type of material and the thickness of the cloth.

AT1/3a,4b; AT3/3a

5. Wash day

Age range
Key Stage 2.

Group size
Small groups.

What you need
White cotton fabric, scissors, water – hot and cold, thermometer, coffee or tea (or another similar substance which will stain fabrics), bowls for washing, washing powders (at least one biological powder) rubber gloves, a stop clock or timer.

What will change?	What will stay the same?	What are we trying to find out?

What to do
The children could visit the supermarket to investigate the range of washing powders/liquids on the shelves. Discuss with the children the range of washing powders which they have seen on sale in the local supermarket. Which washing powder do they have at home? Is there any difference in effectiveness in cleaning clothes if they use one powder rather than another.

Ask the children to carry out a fair test to decide which is the best washing powder to remove tea or coffee stains. They will need to consider variables. It may be helpful to list them in a table such as the one shown above.

They should use the same substance for staining each fabric.

• Are all of the washing powders effective on all of the stains?

• How long does it take to remove the stains? They could try soaking the fabrics overnight in a cold solution of the washing powder to see if this makes any difference.

• How are the children going to record their results? They could make a chart and stick their fabric samples on to the chart.

10 a.m

1 a.m

5 p.m.

Investigative skills

The children have asked questions and made predictions. They have carried out a fair test and used appropriate instruments (thermometer) to measure temperature. They have considered a number of variables.

Content

Washing products may be powders or thick, concentrated liquids. They contain soap and/or synthetic detergents to remove dirt from fabrics. They may also contain other chemicals or enzymes to help remove stains at low temperatures. Some chemicals in the washing powders help to disperse the dirt and hold it off the fabrics in the wash water. Some powders contain an oxygen-based bleaching agent to help remove stains. The washing powders are usually perfumed so that the clothes will smell fresh and clean.

Further activity

The children could try testing the washing powders on fabric stained with protein such as egg or gravy. Are biological washing powders more effective at removing these stains? At which temperatures are these powders most effective?

AT1/4a,4b; AT3 PoS(i)

6. Hard or soft?

Age range

Key Stage 2.

Group size

Small groups.

What you need

Shallow glass dishes, a teaspoon, tap water – if possible from a variety of locations, 2 identical jam jars with tight-fitting lids, hard and soft water samples, a bowl of warm water, thermometers, soap flakes, measuring cylinder.

What to do

The children could consider the amount of water that they use every day. What do we use water for? How does the water which comes out of our taps reach our homes? What is in water?

Ask the children to carry out the following activity to see whether tap water is pure water. They should measure a spoonful of each water sample into a different dish and then leave the dishes in a warm place (near a radiator). They should observe the water samples over a period of time.

What do they think would happen? The water will evaporate and leave some white marks on the glass dishes. Ask the children to look closely at these white deposits. What do they think they are? These are the solids that were dissolved in the tap water.

Discuss the origin of these solids with the children and the effect they may have in the washing process. In some areas of the country the solids cause a problem by 'furring' the kettle, that is, causing a scale to form on the kettle. Introduce the terms 'hard' and 'soft' water.

The children can investigate what happens when soap flakes are added to water. Is there a difference with hard and soft water? What variables will the children have to consider? They will need to measure the same amount of each type of water into identical jam jars. They should add equal amounts of soap flakes to each jar of water and they should warm the water samples up to the same temperature by standing the jars in a bowl of warm water for the same time period. Once the soap flakes have been added the lids should be put on the jars and each jar should be shaken an equal number of times. Careful observations should be made after shaking. In which jar is a lather formed? What else can be observed in the jars?

Investigative skills
The children have made observations, asked questions, suggested ideas and made predictions. They have carried out a fair test and considered the variables involved.

Content
Some water samples do not lather well with soap but form a scum. The soap is reacting with the dissolved solids to form a scum. These water samples are said to be hard. Hard water is caused by dissolved calcium and magnesium compounds in the water.

Hard water is found where the water passes through areas where there are calcium or magnesium salts in the underlying rocks, for example, limestone rock. Hard water causes deposits to be built up in kettles and hot water pipes. NB – *Soft water* can be obtained in hard water areas by using distilled water.
Hard water can be obtained in soft water areas by standing a piece of blackboard chalk in 500ml of water for 24 hours.

AT1/2b,4a,4b

7. Whole investigation – the conditions yeast needs to grow

Age range
Key Stage 2.

Group size
Small groups.

What you need
Sugar, dried yeast, a number of test tubes or small jars, balloons (not new balloons), water, a timer, thermometers, spoons.

What to do
How do I introduce the investigation?
Bring different types of bread into the classroom including some 'flat' breads like chapattis or Mexican tortillas. Discussion about different types of bread could follow. Encourage the children to question why some breads are flat and others are not. What makes bread rise? Introduce the fact that in most bread-making, yeast is the raising agent. (Another raising agent could be bicarbonate of soda.) The bread dough rises because of the carbon dioxide produced by the yeast.
What questions might the children ask and what hypotheses might they make?
What happens when yeast grows? An initial investigation can be carried out using some dried yeast, a small jar or test tube, and a balloon. The children can observe changes over a period of two hours. They should half-fill the test tube with warm water, add a teaspoon of sugar and a little yeast. Tell them to stretch a balloon over the top of the

tube and watch what happens over a period of two hours. They should make regular observations – after 5, 10, 15, 20, 30 minutes then every 15 minutes. This is an appropriate point for a discussion about yeast.

The investigation can then be taken further. The children might ask questions such as, 'What happens if we use cold water?', or 'Will the balloon still fill with gas if we leave out the sugar?' They might suggest that a warm temperature is important for the yeast to grow or that the amount of sugar is important. They should now be asked to design an investigation to find out what conditions yeast needs to grow.

What observations might the children make?

The children should be encouraged to observe the yeast mix. They might comment on the bubbles in the mix, the amount of expansion of the balloons or the appearance of the yeast before it is put into solution.

Designing the investigation, variables involved, fair testing, testing the hypothesis

The importance of a 'fair test' should be emphasised. *(AT1/ 3c, 4b)* What variables are involved? It is useful for the children to decide the following:

• What are they trying to find out and how they will measure this?
• What will change during the investigation?
• What conditions need to be kept the same?

The children could work in groups. Some groups could investigate the effect of temperature on yeast growth, and others could investigate how essential sugar is for growth. If temperature is to be investigated, a range of temperatures should be selected *(AT1/5b)* while other variables remain constant, for example, amount of sugar, amount of water, size of container, number of swirls of container when mixing. They could try leaving out the yeast or use fresh yeast instead of dried yeast. They could bake the yeast in a hot oven before use.

How will the children record their findings?

The children will need to make regular observations (at timed intervals). They could record their results in a variety of ways, for example, in a table, through pictures, and then making group presentations.

Interpreting results

Encourage the children to consider different explanations for the yeast producing more gas at warmer temperatures and in the presence of sugar. *(AT1/5c)* How do these explanations match up with their original hypotheses?

What else might the children investigate?

The children could now investigate the factors that affect the rate at which bread dough rises. *(AT1/5a)*

Content

Risen bread is made with yeast and is light and airy. Yeast is a fungus which grows best at a temperature of 24–29°C. It needs a supply of water and food (usually sugar) to grow. It grows by a process called budding and produces chains of new cells. As it grows it produces carbon dioxide which makes the bread dough rise. When the bread is baked, the heat kills the yeast so that it stops producing carbon dioxide and the bread stops rising.

(AT2/2a,3a; AT3/4a,4b)

CHAPTER 15

Weather and seasons

The British are obsessed with the weather or so it is said. The weather affects what children wear, what games they play and where they play them. Holidays may be made or ruined by inappropriate weather and people's lives can be adversely affected by extremes of rain, snow or drought. In recent years the clearly defined seasons have become more blurred as winters have been relatively mild, and long autumns have followed long springs.

Children will increase their understanding of weather by investigating it at first hand. Early on, children may consider the seasons, the type of weather associated with them and the clothes they need to wear. They can investigate the effects of weather on gravestones, statues, buildings, rocks and landscapes. During heavy rainfall, children might raise a question such as 'where does all the water go?' This would lead to investigations of drainage in soil.

Later, children might investigate whether it is warmer in the morning, at noon or in the afternoon or ask the question, 'is it warmer in the soil, air or water?' The concept of the water cycle and the role evaporation plays, could be highlighted by reference to an investigation on cloth drying under different conditions. This could then be followed up by more detailed references to the water cycle and to the physical processes involved. A whole investigation is described which looks at wind speed. This allows children to ask questions, make hypotheses, design and carry out a fair test and to interpret their results.

The Water Cycle

BACKGROUND

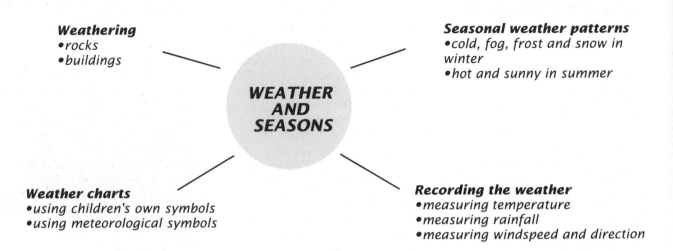

Weathering
•rocks
•buildings

Seasonal weather patterns
•cold, fog, frost and snow in winter
•hot and sunny in summer

WEATHER
AND
SEASONS

Weather charts
•using children's own symbols
•using meteorological symbols

Recording the weather
•measuring temperature
•measuring rainfall
•measuring windspeed and direction

Activity	AT1	Statement of attainment
1. The seasons and the weather	1a, 2b	– Observe
2. Weathering – rocks and buildings	1a, 2b 2a, 3a 2c	– Observe – Ask questions, suggest ideas – Interpret results
3. Soil drainage: where does all the water go?	3b 3d	– Observe and measure – Interpret results
4. When or where is it warmer?	4b	– Measure and manipulate variables
5. When is it warmest?	4a 4b 4c	– Question and predict – Observe and measure – Interpret results
6. Increasing evaporation	4a, 5a	– Question, predict and hypothesise
7. Whole investigation – weather and wind speed	Level 4	

ACTIVITIES

1. The seasons and the weather

Age range
Key Stage 1.

Group size
Pairs.

What you need
Pictures of people in typical scenes from each of the four seasons, a chart to collate weather records for the last few days, weeks or months.

What to do
Ask the children to look at the pictures which are associated with different types of weather and hence seasons of the year. Write on the board the names of the four seasons of the year in cyclical order. Ask them to draw pictures or write a paragraph which describe the weather in each season and the types of clothes they might be wearing. This could be backed up by recording the weather on a daily basis so that the weather in July, October, January and April could be compared.

Investigative skills
The children have been given experience of observing familiar events such as the weather, and the clothes they wear in the summer and the winter. They should explain their picture to other groups. If pupils record the weather on a daily basis they will have practice of making a series of related observations.

Content
By using words and pictures to describe their observations and experiences of the weather and seasons, the children will have shown that they recognise seasonal weather patterns, events associated with the seasons, for example, leaf fall in autumn, and how they dress differently in response to the weather.

AT1/1a,2b;
(Geography AT3/2a)

classroom activity will help them to understand that there are substances in rain water (acid rain) which weather rocks over a long period of time, as opposed to the speedy reaction (weathering) with vinegar. Children should be reassured that they will not weather if they get caught in the rain!

Further activity
More able children might be encouraged to add a description to their observations of weathering in the environment and classroom, of how and why buildings and rocks weather.

AT1/1a,2a,2b,2c,3a; AT3/3c,3d

2. Weathering – rocks and buildings

Age range
Key Stage 1 and 2.

Group size
Small groups.

What you need
Limestone rocks, other types of rocks, vinegar, dropper pipette, tile, board or tray.

What to do
Take the children on a walk and look for evidence of weathering on gravestones, statues and buildings. If in the countryside, look for evidence of weathering on rocks or cliffs. The children should record their findings in pictures and writing.

Follow up the work in the classroom by observing the effects of vinegar on a variety of rocks. Using a dropper pipette, drop 1 or 2 drops of vinegar on to limestone and other rocks. Encourage the children to ask questions such as 'What will happen when we put the vinegar on the rock?'. Some children might predict that 'The softer rock will crumble but the hard ones will not.' or 'The white one will break up but the others will not.' Allow the children to record their observations and to compare what they found out with what they expected to find out.

Investigative skills
The children will have observed familiar materials and events; will have asked questions, suggested ideas and made predictions; will have made a series of related observations of the effect of vinegar on rocks and will have compared their observations with what they expected to find out.

Content
During the walk, children will have observed some of the effects of weathering on buildings and rocks. The

3. Soil drainage: where does all the water go?

Age range
Key Stage 1 and 2.

Group size
Pairs.

What you need
Two or more different types of soil (sandy and clay, for example) which have been collected on the same day and from a similar position; weighing scales, two plastic filter funnels, filter paper if available; two 50cm³ measuring cylinders, two 100cm³ measuring cylinders containing water.

What to do
Water some of the plants in the classroom and ask the children to observe what happens. They will notice that the water 'disappears' and hopefully see that this occurs

at different rates. Explain to them that the water drains into and through the soil and that it associates with the particles of soil. Some of the water comes out of the bottom of the pot.

Show the children the soils and let them look at them and touch them to observe the differences. Ask the children to suggest ideas for a test (strand (i)) or ask them which will let more water through? Ask for predictions and for possible reasons why one soil might drain better than another, for example, 'Because it is gritty.' or 'Because it is sticky.'

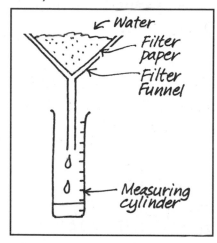

Figure 1

Fold the filter paper twice and open up into a cone shape, before placing it into the filter funnel. Repeat for the other funnel. Talk about adding the soil and ask the children how it could be made a fair test. Encourage them to weigh equal masses of soil or to fill the funnels to the same level. Point out that they are going to pour equal amounts of water ($100cm^3$) on to each soil, so that it is fair. By positioning the funnel in another measuring cylinder, the children will be able to measure the amount of water which has drained (see Figure

1). How long should they wait? How can it be made fair? Ask the children to record their results, to say what they observed and how and why it happened.

Investigative skills

The children have been encouraged to observe closely and to measure the water used to pour on the soil samples and to quantify the amount which has drained by using a measuring cylinder.

The children have been able to say what happened in the investigation and to offer a reason why it happened (interpret results).

Content

The children will have been introduced to drainage in soils and to the idea that water will pass more readily through some soil types, such as sandy soils, than through others, such as clay soils. Unexpected results may often be obtained due to different water contents of the soil to start with, and the packing of the soil in the funnel.

Further activity

Small amounts of the two soil samples could be dropped into separate, long, clear, plastic

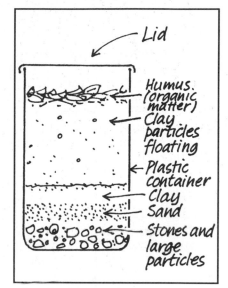

Figure 2

containers of water and the composition of the soil after sedimentation compared. Larger particles (stones) will appear at the bottom of the jar while organic matter will appear on the surface of the water – see Figure 2 above.

Safety

Ensure that the children wash their hands after handling soil and are warned not to put their hands near their mouths.

AT1/3b,3d; AT3 PoS(iv)

	a	**b**
What I want to find out	Air temperature in the morning, noon and afternoon (in degrees Celsius).	Temperature in the air, water and soil at the same time of the day.
What I must keep the same (control)	The thermometer. Location of thermometer. Person reading thermometers.	The thermometers. Exact position of thermometers. Person reading thermometers.
What I must vary/change	The time in the day I take readings: 9.00, 1200, 3.00.	Location of thermometer(s).

4. When or where is it warmer?

Age range
Key Stage 2.

Group size
Small groups or pairs.

What you need
3 spirit thermometers (–10°C to 110°C).

What to do
Remind the children that the temperature of an object is a measure of how hot or cold it is. Discuss the temperature on a hot day, cool day, cold winter day, and of boiling water and ice. Encourage them to talk about temperature in different places and times. Ask them if they would like to suggest an investigation on temperature and/or suggest that they design a fair test to see whether:
(a) it is warmer in the morning, noon or afternoon;
(b) it is warmer in the soil, school pond or air;
Where are they going to put the thermometers? For how long are they going to leave them before taking a reading? Are they going to leave them outside? Help the children to design the fair test using the table above.

Investigative skills
In this activity the teacher has raised questions and hypotheses; the children are given practice of observing, measuring and manipulating variables. They are asked to carry out a fair test in which they select and use thermometers to measure temperature. The variables are relatively easy to control in investigation (a) except perhaps for the need to use exactly the same location (position and height) for the thermometer. In investigation (b), if 3 thermometers are used the only variable to control is the person reading the thermometers. At a more precise level the position of the thermometer in the air, soil and water should be considered.

Content
The children will have had experience of learning how measurements of temperature describe the weather, the variations in temperature during the day and the differences in temperature in different materials at one time.

Further activity
Children could continue the investigation over a period of 5 to 10 days to see if the same pattern is always obtained. Is it the same in the winter as the summer? Some children might be surprised that the temperature of the water in winter is warmer than the air.

Safety
Children should be careful when carrying glass thermometers around the school. These should be carried in their plastic cases. Spirit thermometers should be used in preference to mercury thermometers.

AT1/4b; AT3/4d

5. When is it warmest?

Age range
Key Stage 2.

Group size
Pairs.

What you need
Spirit thermometers (–10°C to 110°C) or maximum/minimum thermometer; data-logging equipment.

What to do
Talk to the children about the temperature during the day and night and the variations which take place. Ask them if there is a general pattern.

When is it often hottest? When is it often coolest?

Ask the children to make a prediction based on prior knowledge or suggest one that they might investigate such as 'It gets warmer during the day and cooler during the afternoon and evening when the sun goes down.'

Inform the children that they must carry out a fair test. Depending on how much experience they have with fair testing, guide them in thinking about where they are going to put the thermometer, where they will put it (in the shade or in the sunlight?) – why is this important? Are they going to leave it in one place (this makes it less difficult to make it unfair). Who will read it and when?

The children should take readings at hourly intervals. A member of staff could take readings later on. The minimum temperature could be recorded but the time of this reading is unlikely to be known though, as it may well be at approximately the time of the dawn.

Encourage the children, or other groups of children to repeat the investigation on another day.

Ask them to analyse the results (data), to look for patterns and to link these to the original prediction/ hypothesis. Alternatively, they could use data-logging equipment with a temperature probe.

Investigative skills

The children might have asked a question or made a prediction about the temperature during the day and night based on their knowledge. They will have been given the opportunity to carry out a fair test and select a thermometer to make temperature readings. In interpreting their results the children will be able to look for patterns and to relate any such pattern, if it exists, to the original question or prediction.

Content

The children will have been given an opportunity to use a thermometer to measure the air temperature outside and this will help them to understand that temperature is one way in which the weather may be described and documented. This may be reinforced by looking at a weather forecast.

Safety

Safety must be stressed as children will be carrying glass thermometers around the school. Spirit thermometers should be used in preference to mercury thermometers.

AT1/4a,4b,4c; AT3/4d

6. Increasing evaporation

Age range
Key Stage 2.

Group size
Pairs or small groups.

What you need
Beakers, tripod, gauze, thermometers, water, heat source such as a spirit lamp or butane burner, safety glasses or goggles. Alternatively, use natural locations such as the cold top of the freezer, a cool place in the classroom and a warm place in the classroom.

What to do

This activity could take place before or after discussion of the water cycle. Talk to the children about wet or damp washing on the line and ask them where they think the moisture goes to? What causes the clothes to dry? Answers such as 'the Sun' or 'heat' might be forthcoming and children might suggest that evaporation will improve or increase with temperature.

Ask them to suggest an hypothesis for the relationship between temperature and evaporation such as 'The higher the temperature the greater the amount of evaporation.' Also get them to suggest a reason for their suggestion (causal link), such as 'This happens because the water (molecules) turn to water vapour (gas) more readily at higher temperatures.'   *Use info*

Ask the children how they might carry out the investigation.

This investigation could be carried out in two ways.

1. Three equal-sized pieces of cloth could be placed in a large amount of water so that they become saturated. They would then be left to dry, one piece on top of the fridge or on a cold surface, another in the cool classroom and the third on top of a radiator. Periodically, they could be examined and qualitatively assessed for dampness. Quantitative measurements are difficult to take in this investigation, except for the temperature of the location in which the material is drying. The time it takes a piece of cloth to dry could be recorded.

2. Equal volumes of water could be placed in three beakers, which are heated at three different temperatures, for example room temperature (approximately 20°C), 40°C and 60°C, for an equal length of time. This will give the children experience of fair testing and manipulating variables. The water loss in the given time may then be recorded, a bar graph drawn and interpretations made.

Investigative skills

The children will have asked a question and/or made a prediction or hypothesis. Children who predict that, 'The higher the temperature, the greater the amount of evaporation.' will be operating at Level 4a, but those that suggest a reason for their suggestion (causal link), such as 'This happens because the water (molecules) turn to water vapour (gas) more readily at higher temperatures.' will be operating at Level 5.

Content

Substances change from a solid to a liquid to a gas as they are heated increasingly. Evaporation of water (changing from a liquid to water vapour, a gas) takes place at temperatures above 0°C, but increases as the temperature increases. The humidity of the air is also important. Evaporation will be faster on a hot, dry, windy day than on a hot, humid, still day. Evaporation is the first important physical process in the water cycle, the other two being condensation and precipitation. Do not use the fridge for a cold place because the cooling unit will increase evaporation. This explains why uncovered food dries up in the fridge.

Further activity
The investigation could be widened to include temperatures from 0°C to 100°C.

Safety
Clearly, the second investigation is an activity with potential dangers. Care needs to be taken with thermometers, glassware, heat sources and equipment after heating. The activity should be avoided if children lack basic practical skills and maturity and, if both the teacher and the other children lack confidence to carry out such tasks.

AT1/4a,5a; AT3/5d

7. Whole investigation – weather and wind speed

Age range
Key Stage 2.

What you need
Simple wind speed device or devices (1–3 in number) made identically or windspeed meter (calibrated), pictures of a windy day, video of a recent weather forecast.

What to do
How do I introduce the investigation?
Talk to the children about the wind, showing them pictures of a windy day and show them the weather forecast on video. Ask them how they could measure wind speed (a simple model could be designed as part of a technology activity, see Figure 1).

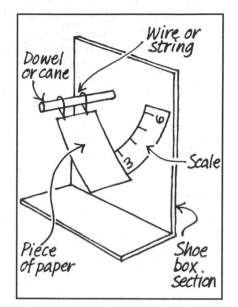

Figure 1

Talk to the children about sunbathing on a windy day and how they might avoid the wind, for example, by lying on the ground or in a position protected from the wind.
What observations might the children make?
The children might have experienced a strong wind as they walk along a road but this weakens as they pass a high hedge or wall (wind break). They might see the clouds moving quickly overhead but observe that it is not very windy on the ground. As the result of their observations of a windy day ask them to think of a question concerning wind speed that they might like to consider.
What questions might the children ask?
The children might ask whether it is more windy in the sunshine or in the shade, in the open or behind a wall, or whether it is more windy at head height than at grass height.
  Ask them to make a prediction such as:
(a) 'It is more windy at head

	a	**b**
What I want to find out	Speed of wind at head height and ground level.	Speed of wind in the open and near/behind a wall.
What I must keep the same (control)	Measuring instrument. Person reading wind speed.	Height of wind speed device. Measuring instrument. Person reading wind speed.
What I must vary/change	Position of wind speed device: 1. ground level; 2. 1m above ground; 3. 2m above ground.	Location of wind speed device: 1. in the open; 2. behind/near a wall.

height than at ground level.' or (b) 'It is more windy in the open than near/behind a wall which is more shielded.' *(AT1/ 4a)*

Designing the investigation
Ensure that the children sit down to plan their investigation for a short time and fill in the investigation form above. *(AT1/4b)*

What will the children record?
Children should record the wind speed in non-standard units with class-made apparatus and in miles per hour or metres per second with commercially-produced devices. Encourage the children to repeat their readings 5 to 10/11 times over a given period. They could then average the results or select the median.

Interpreting the results
The children should be able to draw a conclusion from their findings such as 'The wind is stronger at 2m high than at ground level.' or 'The wind is stronger in the open than near a wall.' They should be encouraged to see a pattern in their results, if one exists, such as, 'The further from the ground the greater the wind speed.' *(AT1, 4c)*

What else could the children investigate?
The children could, over a period of time, relate their wind speed measurements to signs of the wind in the environment, such as smoke rising at an angle and twigs dropping from trees. This could then be compared with the Beaufort Scale of wind speeds.

Content
The children will have found out that it is possible to find out the wind speed and relate this to the weather conditions. They have also found out that the wind speed will vary at different heights and in different locations at the same time. *(AT3/4d)*

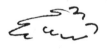

CHAPTER 16

Investigating a story

Stories can provide excellent stimuli for scientific investigations. They can be used to introduce a topic or they can provide a backcloth for a whole range of investigative and cross-curricular activities. Children love reading and listening to stories. Stig of the Dump *is one such story which will motivate and interest children and supply an endless source of ideas for scientific explorations. It is ideal for providing opportunities for developing skills such as observing,* questioning and drawing conclusions. In order that the activities may be relevant it is important that all the children are familiar with this story.

Children could begin by investigating movement using levers. Classification of different types of materials can lead to more complex investigations on insulation and types of fuel, using different ways of collecting and recording information. Many children will be aware of the need to look after our environment and a re-cycling investigation will heighten that awareness. Finally, an examination of the strength of fibres will encourage the consideration of variables and the need to carry out a fair test.

Stories can be used in a variety of ways to support scientific activities as well as providing a limitless range of ideas for cross-curricular work.

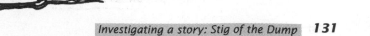

BACKGROUND

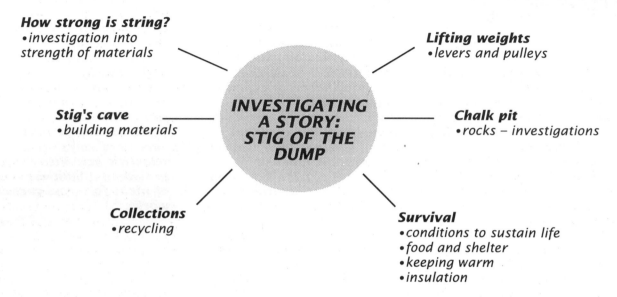

How strong is string?
•investigation into strength of materials

Lifting weights
•levers and pulleys

Stig's cave
•building materials

INVESTIGATING A STORY: STIG OF THE DUMP

Chalk pit
•rocks – investigations

Collections
•recycling

Survival
•conditions to sustain life
•food and shelter
•keeping warm
•insulation

Activity	AT1	Statement of Attainment
1. Lifting with levers	2a 2b	–Question and predict –Observe
2. Working with wood – stick of the dump	2a, 3a	–Question, predict and suggest ideas
3. Keeping warm at home	2b 3a 3d	–Observe –Question –Interpret results
4. The chalk pit	3a 3b	–Predict –Observe and measure
5. 'Can' you recycle?	3a 4d	–Predict –Explain
6. Keep the heat in	4a 4b 4c	–Question –Carry out a fair test –Conclude
7. Whole investigation – which is the strongest string/thread?	Level 4	

The story used in this chapter is Stig of the Dump, by Clive King (Penguin Books)

ACTIVITIES

1. Lifting with levers

Age range
Key Stage 1 and 2.

Group size
Small groups.

What you need
A small block of wood, plank of wood, a heavy load such as a brick or a heavy book.

What to do
'Barney watched the tribesman moving a large slab of rock by using poles as levers.'

A lever is a simple machine invented by early man to help lift heavy loads. The children could predict how many bricks they can lift using a plank and a small block of wood. They should make a lever by balancing the plank over the block of wood. Pressing down on one end of the plank should lift the brick up. This activity could be done on a larger scale in the hall or playground. Can the children lift each other using a simple lever, that is, a large plank of wood balanced on a piece of wood? They could investigate different kinds of levers to see how they work, for example a spade, a tin with a lid and a spoon.

Investigative skills
The children have carried out an investigation in which they have asked questions, for example, 'How many bricks can I lift using the simple lever?'. They have made predictions and carried out tests.

Content
Levers work by increasing the pushing force underneath a heavy weight so that it can be moved with a small effort. There are different types of levers but all have a pivot on which the lever turns. Many tools are simple levers.

AT1/2a,2b;
AT4/3c PoS(ii)

2. Working with wood – stick of the dump

Age range
Key Stage 1 and 2.

Group size
Pairs.

What you need
A collection of small off-cuts of different types of wood (available from a timber yard) and other small objects made of wood, for example, tooth pick, clothes peg, lollipop sticks; magnifiers, a magnet, a bowl of water, a nail.

What to do
The children are going to investigate a number of different types of wood, and group them according to their characteristics. Label or number each piece of wood. First ask the children to make observations of the pieces of wood and to sort them into groups on the basis of these observations. They should observe differences in colour, and in the grain of the wood. Is the wood rough or smooth? The children should then use the magnifiers to make detailed observations. Ask the children to carry out the following tests on the pieces of wood.
• Can the wood be scratched easily with a nail?

- Do all the pieces of wood float in water? Ask the children to suggest their predictions before they carry out this test.
- Are any of the pieces of wood magnetic?
- Weigh the pieces of wood. Design an investigation to see whether the wood absorbs water.
- Can the children now classify the pieces of wood into different groups as a result of these further tests?
- The children could devise their own method of recording their results.

Investigative skills
The children have been making close observations and suggesting questions, ideas and predictions, based on everyday experience, which can be tested.

Content
Wood is a natural material from trees.

Further activity
The children could list all the objects in the classroom which are made of wood and investigate different uses of wood, for example, furniture, insulation (saucepan handles), and so on.

AT1/2a,3a; AT3/2a,3a

3. Keeping warm at home

Age range
Key Stage 1 and 2.

Group size
Individuals or pairs.

What you need
Pencils, paper, clipboards, rulers, photocopiable page 189.

What to do
Tell the children that they are going to investigate how they keep warm at home. Do they, like Stig, have an open fire, or do they use more modern methods of keeping warm? 'My Grandfather always says wood warms you twice, once when you cut it and once when you burn it.' Ask the children to carry out a survey of their friends and neighbours to find out how they keep warm. Discuss different forms of heating with them, for example, gas or oil fired central heating, electric fires, gas fires. Ask them to find out how their homes are insulated to stop the heat escaping. Do they have double glazing? Is the hot water tank lagged? They will need to find out many of the answers to these questions from their parents. This is an opportunity to introduce terms such as 'insulation' and 'lagging'.

Give the children time to plan the questions they will ask and the method they will use to record their results. Much discussion may be needed here. How are the children going to share their results when they return to the classroom?

One example of a recording sheet is supplied on photocopiable page 189.

Compare Stig's home with a modern home in relation to heating and insulation and fuel/energy sources.

Investigative skills
The children have designed an investigation, asked questions and drawn conclusions. They have considered different systematic methods of recording the information they have discovered. They have interpreted the data they have collected.

Content
Homes can be heated by a variety of methods using different fuels such as gas and electricity. Insulation is achieved through double glazing, lining the roof space and walls of houses with a layer of warm material and lagging the hot water tank. Lagging is material used to eliminate loss of heat.

AT1/2b,3a,3d; AT4/3b

4. The chalk pit

Age range
Key Stage 1 and 2.

Group size
Small groups.

What you need
A collection of rocks including chalk; magnifiers, nails, vinegar, a hammer, a cloth bag, safety glasses, magnets, droppers, shallow dishes, bowl of water.

What to do
Stig made his home in a chalk pit: 'If you went too near the edge of a chalk pit the ground would give way.' Tell the children that they are going to investigate the properties of some rocks including chalk. They need to find out as much as possible. Discuss with the children ways in which they can do this. Some helpful suggestions:
- What colour is the chalk? Is it rough or smooth? Does it shine or glisten?
- Are there any fossils in it?
- Examine the chalk with a magnifier. Is it made up of small particles or crystals?
- Estimate the weight of the piece of chalk.
- Does the chalk contain lime?

To find out, scrape off a small amount, put it in a shallow dish and add a drop of vinegar. What can you see happening?
• How hard is the chalk? Scratch it with a nail.
• Does the piece of chalk float or sink? Put the chalk in a bag and tap it lightly with a hammer to crush some of it into a powder. Feel the particles of the powder. Are they coarse or fine? Look at them with a magnifier. Are there any layers in the rock?
• Discuss with the children how they are going to record and communicate their results, for example: a chart, a poster, drawings, a presentation to the rest of the class.

Investigative skills
The children have been designing an investigation using a range of skills including observing, formulating hypotheses, predictions, drawing conclusions, communicating and recording.

Content
Chalk is white, fine-grained and soft, crumbly limestone, consisting of calcium carbonate and minute organic remains. The acid vinegar will react with the chalk to produce the gas, carbon dioxide. The children will see the chalk 'fizzing' when they carry out this test.

Safety
If the rocks are to be broken, safety glass should be worn as an extra precaution.

AT1/3a,3b; AT3/4c

5. 'Can' you recycle?

Age range
Key Stage 1 and 2.

Group size
Whole class followed by small groups.

What you need
Disposable gloves, a large selection of bottles, cans, different types of paper, plastics, pieces of scrap material (cloth), magnets.

What to do
Barney and Stig used their cans as a chimney. How many different uses can the children think of for the cans? Then show the other items (bottles, etc.) and ask the children which items they think can be recycled. Tell the children they must always wear the disposable gloves when handling waste materials. Put the class into small groups of 5 or 6 so that each has a different recyclable item. Go round the class discussing how they can be used. Where are the local collection points for the waste materials?

Ask the children to bring in used drink cans and make a collection. The children can once again work in small groups. Give each group a magnet, and tell them that cans can be made of different metals which are all magnetic except for aluminium. Ask the children to sort the cans into two groups (aluminium and non-aluminium) using a magnet. The children should be asked to predict what will happen when they test the cans with the magnet. Discuss with the children the advantages and disadvantages of recycling.

Investigative skills
The children have been making observations and suggesting ideas and predictions based on everyday experience.

Content
Many types of material can be recycled. The material can be taken to local collection points which include bottle banks and facilities for collecting aluminium cans.

Safety
Care must be taken when handling waste materials. Disposable gloves should be worn at all times.

AT1/3a,4d; AT4/2a,5c

Aluminium Cans

Types of variables		
What will stay the same?	**What will be changed?**	**What am I trying to find out?**
•Size of drinks can •Size of material •Initial water temperature •Times of temperature reading •Amount of water in can	•Type of insulating material	•Final temperature of water after a specified time

Table 1

6. Keep the heat in

Age range
Key Stage 2.

Group size
Small groups.

What you need
Five tins (used drinks cans) of the same size, thermometers, scrap materials for insulation including newspaper; elastic bands, hot water, stop clock, measuring cylinder.

What to do
Stig and Barney kept the draught out of their cave with an insulating layer of red clay – 'Good damp squidgy stuff.' Discuss with the children how they might keep warm outside on a cold day. How do we keep warm at home and how do we prevent heat loss from the house? The idea of insulation should be introduced.

Discuss with the children how they would plan an investigation to find the 'best' insulating material to keep water hot in a drinks can. Ideas such as 'fair test' and 'variables' should be considered. The children will need to decide when, what and how to measure. How are they going to measure quantities such as volume of water and temperature?

Which of the materials available do the children think will best keep the water hot? They could wrap a piece of material around each of the drinks cans. Each can should be covered with a different type of material. One can should be left uncovered. Why? Decisions need to be made such as how the cans will be wrapped, and if it is necessary to have the same size piece of material for each can. How is the material to be secured to the can? Should the same amount of water be put into each can? Will each can have to be filled with water at the same time? Should the temperature readings be taken at the same time? How regularly should temperature readings be taken? When will the children stop taking the temperature reading? Which things should be kept the same and which things will be changed in the test? In consideration of variables it is a good idea if the children fill out a table like Table 1.

The children should be encouraged to devise a table/

Table 2

Temperature readings of water in cans				
Temperature reading of water in can (°C)	Can 1	Can 2	Can3	Can 4
Time of temperature measurement				
Immediately				
After 1 minute				
After 2 minutes				
After 3 minutes				
After 4 minutes				
After 5 minutes				
After 6 minutes				

chart such as Table 2 on which to record their results.

Investigative skills
The children have used a range of skills in this investigation. They have considered the idea of a fair test, asked questions, suggested ideas and made predictions, based on some prior knowledge, in a form which could be investigated. They have observed, hypothesised, carried out practical work, and used measuring instruments. Different types of variable have been considered. The children have interpreted their findings and drawn conclusions from their experimental evidence.

Content
Hot water tanks are lagged, that is, covered with a thick layer of material in order to insulate them and prevent heat loss. Other types of insulation in houses are cavity wall insulation and roof insulation.

The can which is left uncovered will cool the quickest.

Insulation is achieved by trapping a layer of air which prevents heat loss.

Roof lofts can be insulated with felt or glass fibre. To stop heat loss in the cavity between inner and outer walls, it is possible to pump in polystyrene foam. The foam has air trapped in it and is a poor conductor of heat. Double glazing also traps air in a layer between two pieces of glass.

Safety
Water should be heated in a kettle and poured into the cans by an adult.

AT1/4a, 4b, 4c; AT3/3a

7. Whole investigation – which is the strongest string/ thread?

Age range
Key Stage 2.

Group size
Small groups.

What you need
Scissors, tape measure or ruler; a selection of different strings or threads; a wooden board approximately 40cm × 8cm, 2 clamp stands, sets of weights, hooks, drawing pins, sellotape.

What to do
How do I introduce the investigation?
This investigation can be developed in a number of ways.

Read the story *Stig of the Dump* to the children.

Introduce the investigation through discussion. Collect various types of string and threads.

Suggest to the children that they could investigate the strength of fibres, string and threads. They could start by sorting and classifying by type, thickness and texture. Similarities and differences can be observed including close observations using magnifiers and microscopes. The elasticity of the fibres could also be investigated.
What questions might the children ask and what hypotheses might they make?
Encourage the children to ask questions such as the following.
• Is the string/thread made of a number of fibres twisted together?
• Is the thread/string man-made or of natural origin?
• Which of the strings/threads is strongest? Are thick strings/threads stronger than thin strings/threads?

The strongest fibre was...

• Which of the string/threads stretch? *(AT1/4a)*

The children might make the following hypotheses.

• Thick strings/threads are stronger than thin strings/threads.

• If you increase the number of threads in knitting wool, (for example, 2 ply, 3 ply) you make it stronger.

• Wet threads are more elastic than dry threads.

• The thinner the thread the more it will stretch.

What observations might the child make?

A range of observations can be made starting with superficial observations – simple sorting and classification – stretching and feeling (texture). Similarities and differences can be observed. Thickness (number of fibres twisted together) of the strings could be identified. Use a magnifier to look at the coarse structure. Unwind or fray the strings/threads and look through magnifier. Also make observations using a microscope. *(AT1/3b)*

Designing the investigation, variables involved, fair testing, testing the hypothesis.

The children should consider which is the strongest string/thread. How many strings/threads will be tested? Will the strings/threads be composed of one or many fibres? Is it a fair test? What are the variables? What will change, what will remain the same, what will be measured? Length of string, thickness of string, number of weights and time to bear weights should be considered at this stage. How will strength be measured? What resources will be needed?

The children should cut equal lengths of string/thread. (If these are made up of more than one fibre, they should use equal numbers of fibres). They could suspend the threads from a piece of wood by a drawing pin (same number of turns of thread on the pin) as described below.

Cut the strings/threads into equal lengths – approximately 30cm. Suspend the wooden board between two clamp stands and attach the drawing pins to the board at equal intervals across the board. You will need one drawing pin for each piece of string/thread.

Make a small loop at one end of each string/thread and attach each one to a drawing pin. Tie a hook on the other end of the string/threads and secure each with a piece of sellotape. There should be equal lengths of threads between the pins and hooks. Add a 50gm weight to the first hook and continue to add weights until the string/thread breaks. Record the weight on the hook at the time the string/thread breaks. Repeat with each piece of string/thread. *(AT1/4b)*

How will the children record their findings?

The children could make a simple chart such as the one below. Stick a piece of each thread onto the chart and record the weight at the time the string/thread broke.

Each group should report back their findings to the rest of the class.

Interpreting the results

The children could draw a conclusion using their findings, for example, 'The strongest thread was...; the weakest was...' *(AT1/4c)*

Content

String is made up of a number of fibres. Some fibres are man-made, others come from either plants or animals, for example, cotton fibres come from the cotton plant, nylon thread is manufactured from oil and coal.

What else might the children investigate?

The children could now investigate elasticity of the strings/threads. *(AT3/3a)*

String thread	Sample piece of thread	Weight
Silko cotton Darning wool		300gm 250gm

CHAPTER 17

Energy

Energy is an abstract concept. It cannot be seen but its effects can be. This makes it a potentially difficult idea for children to understand. However, they will be familiar with comments such as, 'I do not know where you get the energy', and will have heard of energy sources in films and technological games.

The key idea for children to appreciate is that of energy transfer. Energy in its various forms (movement, electrical, sound, heat, light, nuclear) may be converted or transferred from one form to another. Each time this happens some energy is utilised as heat energy. At Key Stage 2, children may investigate these ideas by heating food and seeing that the food or chemical energy is transferred to heat and light energy. Similarly, electrical energy is converted by belts or pulleys in simple vehicles which the children might make, or energy stored in the elastic band (potential energy) of the bottle roller is converted to movement energy (kinetic energy) as the bottle is released.

Children's early understanding of energy may be developed by investigating the temperature of water, whether things burn or not and by seeing how far a vehicle will travel down a ramp from different starting positions. The last example is the focus of a whole investigation for younger children. There are a host of motivating practical investigative activities which can be used to develop children's understanding of energy.

BACKGROUND

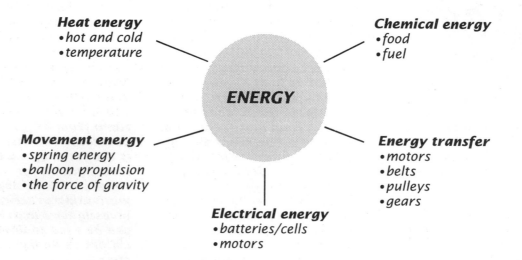

Activity	AT1	Statement of Attainment
1. Hot or cold	1a, 2b	– Observe
2. Fuels and energy	2a 2c, 3d	– Predict – Interpret results
3. How far does it roll?	2b, 3b	– Observe and measure
4. How much energy?	4a, 5a 3b, 4b 3c, 3d, 4c	– Question, predict, hypothesise – Observe, measure and manipulate variables – Interpret and evaluate
5. Springing into action	4a 4b	– Question, predict – Measure, manipulate variables (fair test)
6. The bottle roller	3a, 4a, 5a 3b, 4b, 5b 3c, 3d, 4c, 5c	– Predict and hypothesise – Observe, measure and manipulate variables – Interpret and evaluate
7. Whole investigation – moving vehicles at Level 2	Level 2	

ACTIVITIES

1. Hot or cold

Age range
Key Stage 1.

Group size
Pairs.

What you need
Large bowls of hot, cool and cold (refrigerated) water, spirit thermometers (–10 to 110°C) or digital thermometers for easier reading.

What to do
Recite the rhyme below (or another one about hot and cold, familiar to the children).

As a rule a man's a fool,
When its hot he want it cool,
When its cool he want it hot,
Always wanting what is not.
(Anonymous)

Talk to the children about the meaning of hot and cold. Get them to place one hand in the hot water (40°C) and one hand in the water which has been in the fridge (4°C). Ask them to describe how each hand feels; is the water hot or cold? After 30–60 seconds get the children to place both hands in the cool water. What do they notice? Explain to them that the body sometimes gets confused about the temperature of things and that it is better to use a thermometer which measures how hot or cold something is.

Investigative skills
The children will have observed familiar materials and events and will have had the opportunity to make a number of observations about water at different temperatures.

Content
The children will have gained a greater understanding of the temperatures of various objects and materials. They will be able to compare these with the temperature of their own bodies and come to a better understanding of hot and cold.

The teacher should be aware of the difference between temperature and heat. While heat is a form of energy, temperature is a measure of the amount of heat (how hot or cold an object is). A teapot containing hot tea and a cup of tea may be at the same temperature but there will be much more heat energy in the teapot than the cup because there is more liquid in the former than the latter.

Further activity
The children could measure the temperature of various locations around the school, such as the fridge and above a radiator.

Safety
Ensure that the 'hot' water is not too hot! Thermometers are made out of glass and should be handled with care. Purchase spirit thermometers in preference to mercury thermometers.

AT1/1a,2b; AT4/2b

2. Fuels and energy

Age range
Key Stage 1 and 2.

Group size
Whole class or half of class.

What you need
Photocopiable page 190, samples of coal, wood, stone, candle wax, bread, biscuit, peanut, broad bean (green), paper, metal, or other items which may or may not burn, gas (if available), spirit or butane burner. Try to make the items similar in size to reinforce the idea of a fair test.

What to do
Organise the children at a safe distance from the heat source. Talk to them about the things (fuels) which we use to heat our homes or on which to power our vehicles. Explain that these are burnt to produce heat energy or movement energy. Talk to them about why we eat food. Ensure that they are aware that we need energy to move, to keep warm and to think and play. Give them photocopiable page 190. Show them each item and ask the children to identify them.

Take each item in turn and ask the children to predict whether they think it will burn and therefore produce energy. Get them to record their prediction on the photocopiable sheet. Now attempt to burn each item and ask the children to record what they see (colour of flame, did it burn for long, did it smoke?). Indicate that you are trying to make it fair by burning similar sized pieces. Ask the children to record the items which will make good fuels.

Ask the children to compare what they expected (their predictions) with what they saw, and try to get them to explain their results.

Investigative skills
Under your guidance the children have made predictions and you have carried out a fair test. Children who are able to compare what they expected (their predictions) with what they saw, are operating at Level 2c, and those that explain their results in terms of some items burning to produce heat or heat energy are operating at Level 3d.

Content
The children will begin to appreciate that a number of items burn and can therefore be used as fuels to produce heat energy. Similarly, some foods provide us with energy. They should talk about the fuels used in their homes (gas, electricity (from coal), wood/logs, coal, paraffin) and those used in different forms of transport (cars – petrol; lorries and cars – diesel; aeroplanes – kerosene; some submarines – nuclear fuel).

Safety
Burning anything in the presence of children is potentially hazardous. Avoid using items which are likely to 'spit'. Ensure there is sufficient ventilation. Seek advice if uncertain.

AT1/2a,2c,3d; AT4/3b

3. How far does it roll?

Age range
Key Stage 1 and 2.

Group size
Small groups

What you need
Model cars or alternative, wood or cardboard slope.

What to do
Children could bring in a small, moving vehicle from home, if appropriate. This may be part of a topic on transport, movement or toys.
Ask the children to roll a model vehicle down a slope.

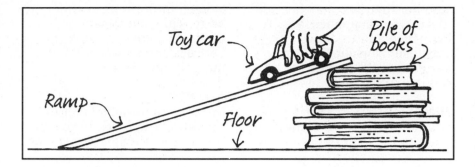

Labels: Toy car, Pile of books, Ramp, Floor

Encourage them to ask questions and make predictions such as, 'What will happen if I release it from the top?' or, 'Will the car go further if the slope is steeper?' How far will the children expect it to go from a given starting point and on a given slope?

Ensure that the children carry out a fair test by starting their cars from the same point each time.

Ask the children to measure the distance travelled by the car. Can they time how long the car was moving? Get the children to record their results.

Investigative skills
The children have carried out an investigation in which they have observed closely and measured the distance covered by the cars, and possibly the time-period the cars were actually moving. The children will develop skills of using equipment and measurement, encouraging them to make decisions about when, what and how to measure. They may also use simple electronic devices, such as digital watches, in their experimental work. They will also have made a series of related observations.

Content
The car moves due to a pulling force called gravity, which pulls all objects towards the centre of the earth. The higher up the ramp the car is released, the further it will move as it has more energy. Pupils should investigate movement using a variety of devices, for example toys and models, which are self-propelled.

Safety
Wooden ramps may be heavy and will cause considerable damage if dropped on small toes.

AT1/2b,3b; AT4/2c,3c PoS(iii)

4. How much energy?

Age range
Key Stage 2.

Group size
Pairs.

What you need
Peanuts, Brazil nuts, digestive biscuits; boiling tubes; mounted needle (e.g. a needle in a cork); clamp stand to support test tube; measuring cylinders; water; heat source; thermometers; scales.

What to do
Show the children the peanuts, Brazil nuts and the biscuits and show them a table of their chemical constituents (see table below). Remind, or point out, to the children that fats contain twice as much energy as carbohydrates per gram. Suggest to the class that you think that the Brazil nut will contain the most energy because it contains the largest amount of fat. Tell the children to write down their predictions and to explain their reasons. Alternatively, show them the energy value of each food and predict that the one with the highest energy value will burn giving off the most heat.

Show the children the equipment for the investigation. Pour 20cm³ of water into a measuring cylinder and pour this into a boiling tube. Take a thermometer and record the temperature of the water. Place a nut carefully on the mounted needle, reminding the children that they must ask you to do this for them, and get it to light by placing it in a flame such as a gas cooker or gas camping stove. Immediately the food is set alight, place it under the boiling tube making sure that

Chemical type	Peanut	Brazil nut	Biscuit (digestive)
Carbohydrate	9g	4g	66g
Fat	50g	60g	20g
Protein	24g	12g	10g
Energy value	2400KJ	2500KJ	1970KJ

as much of the flame is in contact with the tube as possible (see diagram below). As soon as the food has stopped burning take the

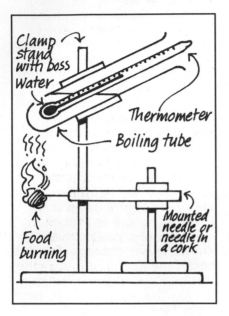

temperature of the water again. Record the result and calculate the temperature increase.

Explain to the children that the food has produced heat energy and that the greater the temperature rise the greater the amount of energy in the food sample.

Encourage the children to think about how they can make the investigation fair. What must they change in each test (the food – independent variable)? What are they trying to find out (the amount of energy/temperature increase – dependent variable)? What must they keep the same in order for the test to be fair (control variables include the amount of water, the weight/mass of peanut, and the distance from the tube that the food is held)?

Ask the children to record their results, to consider whether their test was fair and to say what happened, why it happened and to draw conclusions which link patterns in the results to the original prediction.

Investigative skills
You have suggested some ideas to the children and have made a prediction based on knowledge, which may be investigated. This will help the children make their own predictions based on some relevant, prior knowledge, in the future.

The children have observed and used measuring instruments or have carried out a fair test and selected and used appropriate measuring instruments to measure temperature and volume and possibly mass (weight).

Some children may be aware that their conclusions are invalid because they did not weigh the food sources or keep some of the other variables constant.

Results may have been interpreted at two levels. Some children will be able to describe the results and say that one food had more energy in it than another, while others will be able to say that the foods with the higher fat or energy content gave off the most heat and raised the temperature of the water the most.

Content
The children should be aware that food contains three main chemical types (carbohydrates, fats and proteins) and that these chemical types and the foods themselves contain different amounts of energy. They should be aware that the process of respiration produces energy due to foods reacting gently (burning) with oxygen in the cells of the body. This investigation provides a concrete link between food and energy in a most illuminating way.

Safety
There is an initial danger of mounting the food source on the needle, though this can be carried out by the teacher. Care needs to be taken when burning any substance. The food may be ignited by a long match but it is probably safer to ignite it from a burner even though the temperatures are considerably higher. The boiling tube should not be touched at the end of the investigation and the residue of the foods should be left to cool. The whole activity should be carried out or supervised by the teacher.

AT1/3b,3c,3d,4a,4b,4c,5a; AT2/3a,5a PoS(i),(iv)

5. Springing into action

Age range
Key Stage 2.

Group size
Pairs.

What you need
Materials to build a vehicle: card, spring, two pieces of 4mm dowel (18 and 12cm long); three plastic cotton reels, four rubber grommets or pieces of plastic tubing or rolled up elastic bands, glue gun; tape measure.

What to do
Construct the spring car with the help of the diagram on the next page. Let the children explore the vehicle and encourage them to make it

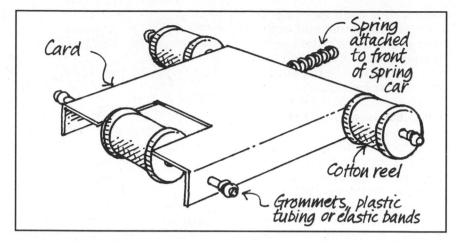

Card

Spring attached to front of spring car

Cotton reel

Grommets, plastic tubing or elastic bands

travel a short, medium and long distance. Remind them about the work they have done on energy and talk to them about where the energy to move the vehicle has come from. Ask them how they made the vehicle go further and relate this to the amount of energy stored in the spring. The children should ask questions, suggest ideas and make predictions and carry out an investigation in an attempt to verify their prediction. They might suggest that 'if the spring was pushed in more, there would be more energy and the car would go further'. How would they make it a fair test? What measurements would they take?

Encourage the children to attempt to quantify how much

the spring has been compressed by relative measurements or preferably actual measurements. They should record their results in a table. Discuss these with the children and help them to interpret them. How do the results fit in with their prediction? Did they carry out a fair test? If the results are surprising, how might they be explained?

Investigative skills
The children have been encouraged to ask questions, suggest ideas and make predictions in a form which can be investigated. They have also carried out a fair test if they started off the car from

the same place on the same surface operated by the same person, and selected and used appropriate instruments.

Content
Chemical energy in our food has been converted into movement energy in our muscles. This allows us to compress the spring against an object. The energy is now stored in the spring, waiting to be released. As the car is released, the energy is transferred from the spring to the body of the car and to the wheels which turn around. This makes the car move. There has been a transfer of energy from our food to bring about movement in the car. The more the spring is compressed, the greater the force that results.

Safety
Some types of glue gun get very hot and molten glue is potentially dangerous. Low temperature guns are available. Remind the children of the dangers of mains electricity.

AT1/4a,4b; AT4/3c,4d,5d

6. The bottle roller

Age range
Key Stage 2.

Group size
Pairs.

What you need
Washing up liquid bottles, 2 pieces of dowel or cane per group – 5cm and 15cm in length, a plastic circle cut from a margarine tub to fit over the neck of the bottle with a hole through the middle (optional), large elastic bands, wire coat hangers cut into a loop to thread elastic band through the bottle.

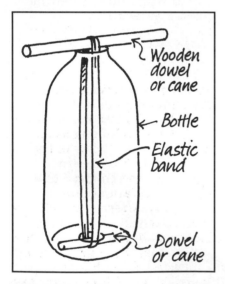

What to do
Let the children construct the bottle roller as shown above. To do this they should remove the nozzle and make a hole in the base of the bottle. They should then select an elastic band which is about half the length of the bottle and push it through the hole at the base of the bottle, securing one end with the smaller piece of dowel. Using the coat hanger bent into a small loop, the children can catch and pull the free end of the elastic band through the neck of the bottle and secure it with the larger piece of dowel. Friction may be reduced by placing a plastic circle between the bottle neck and the dowel.

Allow the children to investigate with their rollers for a while before talking to them about energy. What sort of energy is the bottle roller showing (movement energy)? Where is it coming from/from where is it being transferred (stored elastic energy in the band)? How, and in what form does the energy get into the band (chemical energy in the food is transferred to movement energy through the muscles in the arm and this twists the band)?

Ask the children to carry out an investigation on their bottle rollers. Ask them to suggest ideas and to make predictions or hypotheses saying why they have made them as they have. Remind them to think about energy and how the bottle roller works.

Ensure that they carry out a fair test. What are they trying to find out (independent variable)? What will they have to change systematically to do this (dependent variable)? What must they keep the same (control variables)? What are they going to measure? What will be the range of the dependent variable?

Ask them to draw a conclusion from their investigation. Get them to say what happened, how and why it happened, to look for patterns or trends in their results which link them to the original prediction and to consider if more than one conclusion could account for their results.

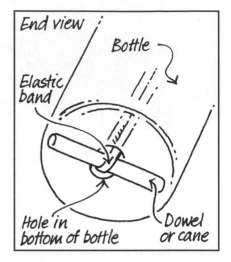

Investigative skills
With regard to questions, predictions and hypotheses, some children may suggest that, 'If you turn the stick around it will move'. Others may state that, 'The more turns of the stick/elastic band the further the bottle will travel', while yet others may suggest that, 'The more turns of the stick the further the bottle will travel due to the greater amount of energy stored in the elastic band'.

With regard to observing, measuring and manipulating variables (fair testing), some children may be able to measure how far their bottle roller travels but not carry out a fair test; others may carry out a fair test and measure accurately the distance travelled by the vehicle with a few turns and many turns, while some children may be able to select the range of the input variables (10, 20, 30, 40, 50 turns) and measure the distance travelled for each.

With regard to interpreting their results and evaluating scientific evidence some children will only be able to conclude that 'The bottle moved because of the elastic band unwinding.' and perhaps

7. Whole investigation – moving vehicles at Level 2

Content
The children should have learned that energy is needed to make things work and that an energy transfer is needed for things to work. The children should be able to identify the energy transfers in a variety of devices. For example in a car, chemical energy in the petrol is burned in the engine and the resulting motion of the pistons makes the axles and wheels move. In the bottle roller, the stored elastic energy in the band is converted and transferred to movement energy of the bottle through the dowel.

Further activity
The children could identify the energy transfers involved in other toys such as those propelled by springs and motors and which use belts and gears.

Safety
Careful use of the wire coat hanger loop will be needed as the cut ends may be sharp.

AT1/3a,3b,3c,3d,4a,4b,4c, 5a,5b,5c; AT4/5b

be able to say that they did not carry out a fair test, when challenged, because they '...did not start their roller from the same place each time'. Other children will be able to conclude that, 'The more turns of the dowel/ elastic band, the further the bottle travelled'. With 10 turns it moved 27cm, with 30 turns it travelled 87cm and with 50 turns it travelled 146cm. Some children might go on to say that the greater movement with more turns is due to the greater amount of energy stored in the elastic band or less friction being produced, but conclude that the former is the more likely explanation for the differences observed.

Age range
Key Stage 1.

What you need
Slope or ramp made of wood, perspex or card; a vehicle.

What to do
How do I introduce the investigation?
Show the children a slope (ramp) and roll the vehicle down the slope a few times with the children's help. Encourage the children to make observations and to ask questions. After a time, change the surface on to which the vehicle is rolling. Compare the vehicle and the slope to riding a bicycle down a hill or slope.
What observations might the children make?
The children should be encouraged to comment on the distance the vehicle rolls from the different starting positions on the slope (ramp), the speed at which the vehicle travels and the distance it travels over different surfaces. They might make other observations such as the straight path (or otherwise) made by the vehicle as it travels down the ramp.

The speech bubble / blackboard reads:

"Will the vehicle go further if it is let go further up the slope?
Why do vehicles go faster on a smooth surface?"

What questions might the children ask and what predictions (hypotheses) might they make?

The children might ask 'Will the vehicle go further if it is let go further up the slope?' and might predict that 'The further up the slope it is let go the further it will go because it is going faster'. *(AT1/2a)* Alternatively they might ask 'Why do vehicles go further on a smooth surface than on a rough surface? and might suggest that, 'On very rough surfaces the vehicles will go much slower.' *(AT1/2a)*

Designing the investigation (variables and fair testing, testing the prediction)

Ask the children for ideas on how to carry out the investigation. Emphasise the importance of the investigation being a 'fair test' and encourage them to keep everything the same except for the thing (variable) they wish to find out.

If it is to see how far the vehicle rolls from different positions on the slope encourage the children to make it a fair test by holding the car in a similar way prior to release. How many positions should you choose so as not to confuse the children? Three positions might be appropriate; near the bottom, half way up and near the top.

If the investigation is to see how far the vehicle travels over different surfaces, encourage the children to carry out a fair test by releasing the vehicle from the same (marked) place each time and by holding the car in a similar way prior to each release.

How will the children record their findings?

The children should record how far the vehicle travels. For instance they might say that 'The vehicle travelled a long way on the floor, quite a way on the cotton material and hardly at all on the carpet.' *(AT1/2b)* Alternatively, they might record the distance travelled in non-standard units such as shoe lengths or number of floor tiles. More advanced children might wish to use standard measures and measure the distance travelled in centimetres. *(AT1/3b)* The children could communicate their findings to their peers and represent their findings in written and graphical forms.

Interpreting the results

Encourage the children to use their observations to support conclusions and compare what they have observed with what they expected. For example they might explain that 'Cars go a long way on the smooth floor, – mine went 12 floor tiles. I did not think it would go that far even on a shiny floor.' Alternatively, they might explain that 'Vehicles go further, the higher up the slope they are released, and less distance the lower down the slope they are released.' 'It went five lengths of my foot when released near the bottom and twelve when released near the top.' 'I knew it would go further when let go from the top because the vehicle is going faster'. *(AT1/2c)*

What else might the children investigate?

The children could try other surfaces or other positions on the ramp or they could see how the slope of the ramp (angle of the ramp) affects the distance the vehicle travels. They could investigate whether other vehicles travel further than the selected one or whether the wheel size affects the distance travelled.

CHAPTER 18

Animals and plants

Animals, and to a lesser extent plants, always captivate children's interest and are therefore a rich source for investigations. It is important that children gain an early understanding of the need to conserve wildlife and their habitats, and that they show animals and plants the respect they deserve. By caring for plants and animals in the classroom under supervision, children will develop this respect and will gain a greater understanding of the needs of animals and plants.

Children should develop their knowledge and understanding of the variety of animals and plants and

this is best done through first hand investigation. A minibeast hunt would be an exciting start to an investigation on animal types, habitats and classification, but a pond study would be a suitable alternative. This may be approached at a range of levels depending on the age and abilities of the pupils.

The wonders of plant growth, diversity and reproduction captures the imaginations of pupils, less than their animal 'relatives'. Yet, apart from not moving and not being sometimes cuddly or scary, plants are equally as fascinating as animals. Children may

discover this by investigating the germination of seeds or the growth of a seedling, find out what plants require to live and sort tree leaves and identify them. Older children may investigate the effects of fertiliser on plant growth and discuss the advantages and disadvantages of their use. The whole investigation in this chapter considers the effects of pollution on plant growth. Hopefully, the children will appreciate plants a little more after carrying out the activities in this chapter. If they do not, just drop it into the conversation that without plants they would not be alive!

BACKGROUND

Variety of living things
•animals (humans), plants
•water and land, animals and plants

Enhance growth
•fertilisers and optimum conditions

Conditions to live
•food, water, warmth, shelter (animals)
•light, water, warmth, soil (plants)

ANIMALS AND PLANTS

External parts
•root, stem, leaf, flower

Sorting/classification
•broad groups – own criteria

Retard growth
•pollutants and poor conditions

Activity	AT1	Statement of Attainment
1. Minibeast hunt; variety is the spice of life	1a, 2b	– Observe
2. Which came first?	2a 2b	– Question and predict – Observe
3. Sorting plants; take a leaf out of my book, bud	2b	– Observe
4. Where are we found?	1a, 2b 2a, 3a 2c	– Observe and measure, – Question and predict – Interpret results
5. What do plants need to live?	3a, 4a	– Question and predict
6. Fertilisers and growth	3b, 4b 3c, 3d, 4c	– Observe and measure – Interpret results and evaluate evidence
7. Whole investigation – pollution and plant growth	Levels 4 and 5	

ACTIVITIES

1. Minibeast hunt; variety is the spice of life

Age range
Key Stage 1.

Group size
Pairs or individuals.

What you need
Collecting trays or specimen containers, plastic spoons or pooters, magnifying glasses, pond net, photocopiable page 191, paper, pencils, access to a pond or school grounds.

What to do
After the necessary preparations allow the children to pond dip or search for minibeasts in the school grounds. For the latter, it is advisable to have an area where large pieces of wood, bricks, cardboard and so on have been left to encourage habitats favoured by invertebrates (animals without backbones).

Tell the children to observe the different animals they find and to make drawings of them using the magnifying glasses. Try to get them to record where they found the animal. Some animals could be collected by using pooters or plastic spoons and specimen containers, with observations taking place in the classroom. Animals may be identified using photocopiable page 191 but there is a danger that the children will draw from the sheets and not from their direct observations of the animals.

The sensitive collection of animals should be discussed with the class.

Ensure that the children have drawn large pictures of at least five animals and have attempted to name them. Encourage them to look for similarities and differences.

Investigative skills
The children have recorded their results in a systematic way by relating the animals found to a particular location. They have had the opportunity to observe animals in their environment and to identify similarities and differences.

Content
The children will have been introduced to the wide variety of animals found in the pond or school grounds. This along with studies of other local habitats and videos (for

of the oceans and the ...ains), will help them ... ...reater ...ding of the ...ferences in shape, size and location of animals (and plants).

Safety
The children should be encouraged to take great care in picking up and observing their animals. They should also be told about the sensitive collection of animals, returning all animals to the wild and about disturbing the habitat as little as possible. Adequate supervision at the pond is essential.

AT1/1a,2b; AT2/1b,2c

2. Which came first?

Age range
Key Stage 1.

Group size
Pairs.

What you need
Broad bean seeds which have

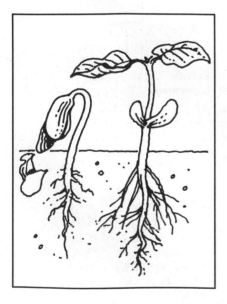

been grown in compost or soil in a deep tray by the teacher or in individual plastic jars with blotting paper by the children; coloured paper with 'youngest' and 'oldest' written on the top left-hand and right-hand corners respectively.

What to do
If the beans have been grown in individual plastic containers they may be viewed in situ, but ordered as suggested below.

If they have been grown in a tray the following could be carried out. Carefully remove the beans from the compost/soil. Lay the beans on a table, possibly on a piece of paper. Let the children look at them and encourage them to ask questions such as 'How long have they been planted?', 'Why are they different?', and 'What are those things?'. Talk to the children about how seeds germinate by taking in water and that some germinate and grow more quickly than others.

Explain to the children that you want them to put 6–8 beans into order with the youngest bean on the left of the paper and the oldest bean on the right of the paper. This could be compared to the human life cycle: baby, child, teenager, young adult, middle aged adult, old adult. Ask the children to draw the beans, stating which are the young and the older ones and to label any parts they know.

Investigative skills
The children will have asked questions of the 'how', 'why', 'what' and 'What will happen if...?' types and may have made suggestions and predictions. By placing the beans in a developmental sequence the children will

have made a detailed series of related observations.

Content
The children will be given an opportunity to name the main parts of a flowering plant, even though the flowers may not have developed yet.

Further activity
A similar activity could centre around the developing buds/flowers of the horse chestnut tree.

Safety
Ensure that the children keep their fingers away from their mouth and wash their hands at the end of the activity.

AT1/2a,2b; AT2/1a, PoS(i)

3. Sorting plants; take a leaf out of my book, bud

Age range
Key Stage 1.

Group size
Pairs or small groups.

What you need
An opportunity to walk in the woods on a fine day (alternatively a collection of tree leaves or twigs); polythene bags or a vasculum to keep the leaves/twigs fresh; paper or card, pencils, adhesive tape or glue.

What to do
Take the children to an area where there is a good mixture of 'native' deciduous trees such as oak, ash, sycamore, hawthorn, elm, lime, beech and some evergreen trees such as holly, yew and pine. Depending on the time of year

collect some leaves or twigs containing leaves if possible. Alternatively, bring a collection of these into school. Ask the children to observe the collection carefully. How might they sort the collection into smaller groups? How many groups might they have (discourage ten groups of one, for example)?

Alternatively, talk to them about sorting things into groups (classification) as they would cars or stamps.

Get the children to sort the collection into sets or broad groups on the basis of an observable characteristic. If the children have difficulties doing this, ask them about the similarities of and differences between the items. Gradually help them to consider leaf shape or bud colour or position of buds and so on.

Ask the children to describe each set, for example, black buds, brown buds, and to stick them on a piece of paper or card.

Discuss with the children how one of their set/broad groups differs from another.

Consider how one group of children have come up with a different solution to another.

Investigative skills
The children have made a series of related observations by looking closely and grouping different types of leaves or twigs.

Content
By using simple features such as bud colour or leaf shape, the children have divided living things into broad groups. They have started to show the elementary beginnings of classification by identifying similarities and differences and by grouping. They have used their own arbitrary categories but will see that other groupings are possible. The teacher might like to point out some other identifying features such as opposite and alternative buds, single or multiple (compound leaves) leaves and buds in clusters.

Further activity
A similar exercise could be carried out with animals found in a pond or around the school grounds (see Activity 1). Features such as the number of legs or body sections, presence of a shell and colour would be used to group the animals.

Safety
Adequate supervision would need to be considered for an out of school activity.

AT1/2b; AT2/2b

4. Where are we found?

Age range
Key Stage 1.

Group size
Pairs or small groups.

What you need
Specimens or photographs/diagrams of some of the following: woodlouse, lady bird, snail or slug, millipede or centipede, greenfly or blackfly, beetle; photocopiable page 192.

What to do
Gather the children around and show them the animals you have collected from the school grounds (alternatively show them the pictures of

these animals). Let them talk about the animals and encourage them to ask questions. If the question has not been asked, enquire of the children where these animals might be found. Do they live in the same places and do they like the same conditions to live?

Some children might have noticed woodlice under plants and bricks, or greenfly on grass, and will be able to make a prediction with guidance such as 'Woodlice are found under plants and stones.'

After a while give out photocopiable page 192.

Explain the sheet to the children, pointing out that they must select an animal, suggest where it might be found and see if it is present in that place and the other places on the sheet. Get them to look under a brick first, then look at some grass, then under some plants and then some dead leaves to make it fair. Ask them to record the numbers of their animal they find.

When the children have returned to the classroom get them to compare where they *thought* they would find their animal with where they *actually* found it.

Investigative skills
The children have probably asked questions and suggested ideas and made predictions.

Some children might have asked questions, made predictions and suggested ideas based on some prior experience which may be tested, such as 'The woodlice are found under the plants in our garden'.

All the children will have had the opportunity to observe familiar things and have make a series of related observations.

All the children will have the opportunity to make a conclusion and will be able to compare it with their prediction (where they would find a particular animal)

Content
Greenfly, blackfly and ladybirds will be found on grasses and other plants such as roses; snails may be found on plant stems and under plants; woodlice will be found under plants, wood and bricks; beetles, millipedes and centipedes will be found under stones and logs, leaf litter, decomposing matter or soil. Worms are found in the soil. The children will find that animals are found in different places.

Further activity
The children could compare the animals found in a pond with those found in the school grounds, or those found on the surface of the water, in the water or associated with the

vegetation and in the mud at the bottom of the pond.

Alternatively they could compare the birds found around the school with those associated with water or woodland.

Safety
Appropriate care and supervision needs to be taken if children are taken to ponds. Ensure that the children wash their hands after handling items such as stones and leaf litter.

AT1/1a,2a,2b,2c,3a; AT2/2c

5. What do plants need to live?

Age range
Key Stage 1 and 2.

Group size
Pairs.

What you need
Yogurt pots, plastic tea cups or plant pots; soil or compost; germinated cress, cereal or pea seeds grown in a seed tray.

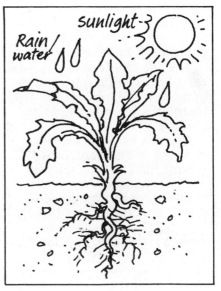

What to do

Ask the children if they have grown any plants at home. Ask them how they grew them and raise the question of what conditions the young plants might need to grow well. The children might suggest that soil or compost, light, warmth and water are needed for growth.

Show the children the young germinated plants growing in a seed tray. Inform the children that they are going to design an investigation to find out if any *one* of the conditions is necessary for healthy growth of the plants. Tell them to write down their plan and to write down their prediction explaining *why* they think the particular condition, for example, light, is necessary. For instance they may say that 'Light is needed or the plants will get long and leggy.' or 'The plants will die without light.'

Remind the children that they must make their investigation a fair test.

Discuss with the children how they will record their results. Ideas such as height of the plants might be mentioned or how healthy the plants appear. Over how many days will they record their results? Ask them to choose one method of recording their results. When they have carried out their investigation ask the children to draw a conclusion based on their results and to relate this to their original prediction.

The teacher should be aware that if pots are placed in the fridge they are actually deprived of warmth *and* light and so the test is not strictly fair. This could be avoided by leaving the fridge door ajar, but artificial light will be involved and use of electricity will increase.

Investigative skills

The children might have suggested that plants need light, or one of the other conditions, because they have seen them growing on the windowsill at home. More able children might be able to state that light is needed for healthy growth or that without light plants will die.

Content

The children will discover that plants need certain conditions to sustain life. Most plants require water, warmth and light to grow though soil is not required in the short term.

One of the variables under investigation will indicate that green plants need light to stay healthy in the short term and to stay alive in the longer term. Plants when deprived of light lose their green colour (for example, grass under a plank), and become long and leggy. While they may grow taller than plants in the light, they will not look so healthy and will eventually die. Plants use the light to make sugars (food) in a process called photosynthesis (photo = light, synthesis = to make by); without light no food is made and death results.

Further activity

The children could continue the investigation above by looking more precisely at one variable (such as water given per day, say 0ml, 5ml, 10ml, 15ml and 20ml) over a range of values (see Activity 7).

The conditions required by plants to grow well could be compared with the conditions that animals need to sustain life. These include food, water, shelter, (clothing).

Safety
The children should wash their hands after handling soil and compost.

AT1/3a,4a; AT2/2a,3c

6. Fertilisers and growth

Age range
Key Stage 2.

Group size
Pairs.

What you need
Bean or cereal seeds grown in a tray; yogurt pots or plastic drink cups or plant pots; sand, a ruler, particle or (preferably) liquid fertiliser.

What to do
If possible take the children to a farm, or invite a farmer, farming representative or chemical representative into school. Ask them to show the pupils some fertilisers (and possibly pesticides), to talk about the costs involved, the benefits in using them, the potential harmful effects and when they are applied. If possible, contact an organic farmer or gardener as well.

Show the children the tray of seedlings and bottle of liquid fertiliser or solid fertiliser. Tell them that you have a prediction to make about plant growth and fertiliser: 'The more fertiliser that is added, the stronger the growth and the more leaves and seeds produced'.

Tell them to put one seedling in a pot of sand, being careful not to damage it. It might be helpful to demonstrate this process and to make small holes in the bottom of yogurt pots and drinks cups. Ask them how to find out if more fertiliser will affect the growth. Clarify that one of the pots will get no fertiliser each week, one will get half the recommended dose and the other will get the recommended dose. How will the test be made fair? How much water should be given each week (the same)? Where should the plants be placed (together near the light)? Have they all been put in the same type of pot with the same amount of sand?

Allow the children to set up the pots and to label them clearly with their names and the treatment to be given. How will they know which is growing better? Would height be a useful measure? Would appearance be useful to record? Could they wait until the seeds are produced and count them or weigh them?

Clearly, if the seeds are to be considered, the investigation will be a long one taking much of two terms, so it may be difficult to maintain motivation for all of the children. There is also a danger of the plants being damaged or dying.

Ask the children to record their results over a period of time and to draw their conclusions. Was it a fair test? Are their conclusions valid? Get them to explain why the plants grew as they did and to discuss any pattern that has emerged.

Investigative skills
The children have been provided with the idea and prediction for this investigation to help them do the same in future investigations. Some children might have shown the ability to carry out a fair test and take appropriate measurements, while others might have only done the latter.

Some children might realise that they used different amounts of water or the plants were in different places in the classroom so the test was unfair and their results were invalid. Children might be able to conclude that the plants with no fertiliser grew 15cm, those with half the recommended dose grew to a height of 17cm and those with the recommended dose grew to 22cm. Some might be able to say that the more fertiliser

that was used the greater the growth and that the teacher's prediction was correct.

Content

The children will have studied an aspect of the environment which is affected by human activity. They will probably have seen the benefits of adding fertilisers to the soil (increased yield, healthier plants) but need to understand that chemicals may have a detrimental effect on the environment, for example when too many nutrients are washed into streams and ponds and when habitats are affected. Fertilisers also affect the soil structure in time.

A very small sample of one plant for each treatment is used which is not good scientific practice. This could be increased, but alternatively, by grouping children's results together larger samples of perhaps 10 (out of a class of 30) might be obtained.

Safety

Children should be warned not to touch fertilisers with bare hands and transfer it with suitable receptacles. Nevertheless they should wash their hands after each activity. A liquid fertiliser is preferable.

AT1/3b,3c,3d,4b,4c; AT2 PoS(iii)

7. Whole investigation – pollution and plant growth

Age range
Key Stage 2.

Group size
Pairs.

What you need

Cress seeds or seedlings; plastic petri dishes or wide and shallow food (margarine) pots; cling film (optional); pollutants such as salt, vinegar, detergent, copper sulphate (beware! see 'Safety').

What to do
How do I introduce the investigation?

The children will have completed some work on pollution and will know that some pollutants affect plant growth and know the ways in which growth is affected. Produce some seeds or seedlings, half of which have been grown in a pollutant and half which have not. Encourage observations and questions. Encourage the children to design and carry out an investigation on plant growth and pollution.
What observations might the children make?

The children will notice that either germination or growth has been affected by the addition of the pollutants.

What questions might the children ask and what hypotheses might they make?

The children might suggest that 'The more pollution added to seeds/plants, then the less likely they are to germinate/ grow well.' Encourage them to give a reason for their prediction such as, 'Less seeds will germinate if the amount of pollution is high because pollutants damage the seed and stop it germinating.' **(AT1/4a)** or 'Less seeds will germinate if the amount of pollution is high because the pollutants will get into the seed and kill (destroy the enzyme reactions going on in) it. **(AT1/5a)**
Designing the investigation, variables involved, fair testing, testing the hypothesis

The children will need to consider what safe pollutants

they could use. Gases and radioactive materials are not practical! They might suggest oil but although it does not mix well with water which is necessary for germination, it could be used particularly if seedlings are used. Salt, vinegar and detergents could be used as could copper sulphate, a poisonous chemical (see below).

The children will need to consider the range of dilutions to use. They might choose 0%, 1%, 5% and 10%, but are more likely to choose dilutions of 100%, 50%, 25% and 0% as the range for the independent variable. The dependent variable will be the number of seeds which germinate or the growth of the plants. The control variables will include the same amount of liquid given to each pot, which will be situated in the same conditions. If children can carry out a fair test and carry out accurate measurements they will have attained level 4 **(AT1/4b)**, but, if in addition, they choose a range of variables to produce meaningful results they will have achieved Level 5. **(AT1/5b)**

How will the children record their findings?

The children will count the number of germinating seeds or measure the growth of the seedlings. Averages may be taken for the growth of the seedlings. Graphs may be drawn showing the effects of the strength of the pollutant on germination or growth.

Interpreting the results

The children should be able to draw conclusions which link their results to the original prediction or hypothesis, such as 'The more pollutant there was, the less the seedlings grew/the quicker they died.' **(AT1/4c)**

Children might evaluate their results and suggest that 'The failure of the seeds to germinate could be due to the pollutant but might be due to no water getting into the seed, or, 'because the seeds were covered with cling film '. They might argue that these ideas are unlikely because there was water in with their pollutant, or, the control seeds grew despite being covered. These children will have shown the ability to evaluate the validity of their results by considering different interpretations. **(AT1/5c)**

What else might the children investigate?

If the children use small dilutions of the pollutants, for example, 50%, 25%, and so on they are unlikely to get any germination and death of the seedlings will result. The investigation could be repeated using dilutions of 10%, 5% and 1%, 0.5% and 0.1%.

Content

The children will have completed some work on pollution and will know that some pollutants may have little effect on plants and animals, that others affect the health and growth of living organisms and that others may kill, for example, Chernobyl, Bhopal. Plant yields such as grain production may be reduced by dust on the leaves and high levels of toxic gases in the air and toxic materials (metals such as copper and lead) in the soil. **(AT2/5c)**

The 0% treatment is the control and indicates if the seeds are germinating or growing well without the pollutants. The results could not be relied upon if these seeds/plants did not grow.

Safety

Ensure that the children keep their fingers from their mouths, that they wash their hands after the activity and that any solution or powder falling on their skin is washed off immediately. Copper sulphate is toxic and should be used with care. Cling film could be used over the growing pots as a safety precaution but this will introduce unnatural growing conditions.

CHAPTER 19

Investigating food

This topic provides an opportunity to investigate the familiar world of food. Our supermarket shelves are filled with an enormous variety of foods but in many countries people are starving. The food we eat affects the way we look and feel, and a balanced diet is essential to keep us fit and healthy.

Scientific investigations with food will help the children to gain a deeper understanding of the importance of food to our health and well-being. They can carry out activities such as observing food ripening, and by baking cakes they can explore the chemistry of mixing ingredients. Children will be encouraged to think about the need for food preservation and why some foods contain colourings and other additives. A whole investigation on bread provides an opportunity to develop a range of process skills using one of the most important foods in our lives.

BACKGROUND

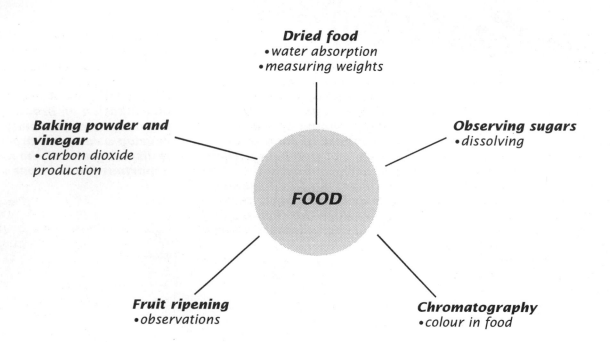

Dried food
•water absorption
•measuring weights

Observing sugars
•dissolving

FOOD

Baking powder and vinegar
•carbon dioxide production

Fruit ripening
•observations

Chromatography
•colour in food

Activity	AT1	Statement of Attainment
1. A spoonful of sugar	1a, 2b	– Observe
2. Warm it up!	1a, 2b 2a 2c	– Observe – Predict – Compare observations with predictions
3. Going brown – bananas ripen	1a, 2b 2a 2c	– Observe – Predict – Conclude
4. Dry it out	3b	– Observe and measure
5. What colour is it?	3d	– Explain
6. Bubbling	4a 4c	– Question and predict – Conclude
7. Whole investigation – bread	Level 2	

ACTIVITIES

1. A spoonful of sugar

Age range
Key Stage 1.

Group size
Small groups.

What you need
A variety of different types of sugar, for example, icing sugar, demerara, soft brown, preserving, caster, cube, granulated; shallow dishes, plastic spoons, hand lenses, transparent plastic cups; cold and warm water.

What to do
This activity can be introduced through discussion. How many children have sugar on their cereal in the morning or add sugar to a cup of tea? Talk to the children about the different types of sugar that are available in a supermarket and when they might use these, for example, icing sugar on birthday cakes, preserving sugar for jam making, brown sugar in fruit cakes such as a Christmas cake or wedding cake. Encourage the children to make close observations of the sugars. How are they the same? How are they different? They could use their hand lenses to look closely at the sugars. How can they describe the different sugars? Do the sugars feel different from each other? Group discussion should be encouraged.

The children will know that sugar 'disappears' (dissolves) when it is stirred into a cup of tea or a fruit drink. Ask them to try and find out whether all of the different types of sugar dissolve. Does the icing sugar dissolve more quickly than the cube sugar?
If so, why?

Results could be recorded on a chart and this can be displayed in the classroom.

Investigative skills
The children have observed the different types of sugars, described them, and tried to dissolve them.

Content
The sugar we eat comes from two plants – sugar cane and sugar beet. Sugar cane is grown in countries with a hot, wet climate and the sugar comes from the stem of the plant. Sugar beet is grown in cooler climates and the sugar comes from the root. Granulated sugar is the main product of the refining process. Caster sugar has finer granules and icing sugar is made by pulverising sugar crystals to a very fine powder. Icing sugar dissolves very quickly. Cube sugar is made from granulated sugar mixed with sugar syrup and moulded into shape, The crystals in preserving sugar are slow-dissolving and it is used for making jam and other preserves. The darker the sugar, the richer the flavour. Demerara sugar has coarse crystals.

Further activity
The children can use some of the sugars to make cakes. Does brown sugar give the cakes a different taste from white sugar?

AT1/1a,2b; AT3/1a

2. Warm it up!

Age range
Key Stage 1.

Group size
Whole class, small groups.

What you need
Eggs, pieces of chocolate, butter, margarine; small foil dishes; a bowl of warm water.

What to do
Ask the children to draw some pictures of food which change when they are heated. A class discussion can encourage the children to describe changes which occur in heated food, for example, when an egg is boiled or when chocolate melts. In order to observe heat changes, different food samples (chocolate and butter) can be put in foil dishes and floated on warm water. (Take care here!) The children should predict what will happen when the foods warm up. What will the foods look like when they have cooled down? Encourage them to make detailed observations and use words such as 'melting', 'solid', 'liquid' as the foods are heated. Ask the children to compare their results with their predictions.

It is also useful to discuss how heat makes some foods change from liquid to solid. The children can compare boiled eggs with raw eggs. (Again take safety precautions here – an adult should boil the eggs.) Do eggs look the same when they are boiled for only 1 minute compared with 4 minutes or 10 minutes? The children should make predictions before testing.

Is it possible to make the solid egg liquid again?

Investigative skills
The children have observed familiar foods being heated and cooled. They have suggested ideas, made predictions and compared their observations with what they expected.

Content
When a solid is heated it melts and forms a liquid. The heat energy makes the particles which constitute the solid move more quickly and a liquid is formed. Chocolate and fats such as butter or margarine will solidify on cooling. Eggs, however, will not return to the liquid state once they have been heated. The proteins in the egg are 'set' or coagulated by heat. If heated for any length of time, the proteins will become tough, hard and indigestible.

Further activity
The children could investigate the effect of adding warm water to jelly cubes.

AT1/1a,2a,2b,2c;
AT3/2b PoS(iii)

3. Going brown – bananas ripen

Age range
Key Stage 1.

Group size
Individuals or small groups.

What you need
Bananas – varying from green to ripe; large shallow dishes or foil.

What to do
Discuss with the children which is their favourite fruit. Talk about ripening fruit. What causes fruit to ripen? How is fruit which comes to us from abroad preserved? How do we know if a banana is ripe or unripe?

The children can investigate the changes which occur in bananas as they ripen. They should make detailed observations of the fruit over a period of time. Can they slow down the ripening process? Does it make any difference to the ripening rate if the bananas are peeled? How quickly do the banana skins

change colour? Ask the children to describe any colour changes in detail. Encourage them to smell the fruit as well as looking at it. The children could investigate the effect of temperature on the ripening process.

Investigative skills
The children have observed familiar fruits and described them in detail. They have asked questions such as 'Why is the banana turning brown?', suggested ideas and made predictions – 'The banana in the warm place will go brown more quickly than the one in the cool place.' They have made a series of related observations – 'The browner bananas smelt stronger than the green/yellow bananas.' They have drawn conclusions – 'Bananas ripen quicker in warmer places.'

Content
When fruit ripens, a number of changes occur.
There is a change in colour, the fruit becomes softer and more sugars are produced in the fruit which then becomes sweeter. The ripening process is accelerated in warmer conditions.

Further activity
The children could investigate what happens when cut apples are exposed to air.

Safety
If the children are going to taste the fruit they must do so under hygienic conditions and wash their hands before tasting. Over-ripe fruit should not be eaten. All surfaces should be kept spotlessly clean.

AT1/1a,2a,2b,2c;
AT2 PoS(iv)

4. Dry it out

Age range
Key Stage 2.

Group size
Whole class, small groups.

What you need
A range of dried foods from the supermarket including dried fruits, pulses, dried mashed potato, soups; a dried complete meal; spoons, weighing scales, graduated cylinders or beakers; paper, pencils, clipboards, rulers.

What to do
A visit to the supermarket is an excellent stimulus for a topic on food. Point out to the children the range of dried food available on the shelves. Talk to the children about the need for preserving food and that one of the oldest methods of preserving foods was by drying it. During the visit to the supermarket (either as a class or ask the children to conduct the survey with their parents) ask the children to carry out a survey of the dried food available. They can classify the foods into different types, for example, soups, dried fruits and so on. Encourage the children to design their own recording sheets for systematic collection of the data.

On returning to the classroom the children can investigate what happens when water is added to dried foods. Using the dried food samples available they could work in their groups to find out how much water the food absorbs and what other changes take place on addition of the water. (Ask them to think about appearance and texture.) They will need to weigh the food before and after the addition of the water. Is there a change in volume? How can this be measured? How long do the foods take to absorb the water? Is all the water absorbed? What happens if more water is added? Encourage the children to make decisions as to how they are going to record their results and communicate them to the rest of the class.

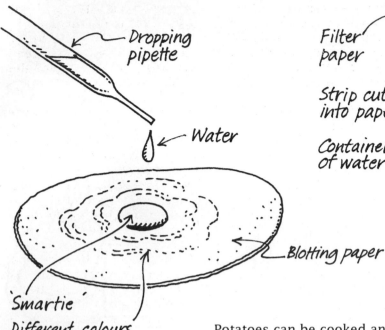

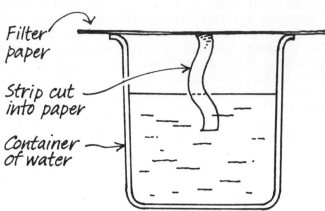

Dropping pipette

Water

Filter paper

Strip cut into paper

Container of water

Blotting paper

'Smartie'

Different colours of food dye

Investigative skills

The children have observed closely and measured weight, volume and time using appropriate equipment. They have systematically recorded their data.

Content

Foods are dried to preserve them. Micro-organisms cannot grow in dried foods. Drying concentrates the soluble ingredients in food and this prevents the growth of bacteria and moulds. There are a variety of methods of drying out food. Some fruits and herbs are naturally dried by exposure to the sun. Some foods are dried by the use of heat in industrial processes. Other foods are freeze dried. This process involves the vaporisation of water when the food is frozen. Correct packaging of freeze-dried food is important as air, light and moisture must be excluded.

Potatoes can be cooked and mashed before drying. The dried powder is granulated and the starch cells reconstituted with water to give mashed potato.

Dried foods are reconstituted by the addition of water.

AT1/3b; AT2 PoS(i)

5. What colour is it?

Age range

Key Stage 2.

Group size

Small groups.

What you need

A box of Smarties; blotting paper or filter paper; water-soluble felt pens; dropping pipettes, plastic cups, water.

What to do

This activity can be introduced by talking about the range of colours of sweets (including Smarties). Which colour of Smarties do the children like best? Does one coloured sweet taste different from another?

Begin the activity by discussing different colours in food – both in natural and processed foods – for example, carotene in carrots, food colouring in sweets. Ask the children to investigate to see what happens when a Smartie is placed on the centre of a round piece of blotting paper or filter paper. What will happen when water is dropped on to the Smartie? They could try using a dropping pipette to put drops of water on to the Smartie. What do they see? Only one drop at a time should be added.

Now that the children have seen that there are a mixture of colours in the Smarties they could go on to investigate colours in inks. Ask the children to see how they could find out how many colours make up the ink in different felt tip pens. They may develop a variety of methods or they could try the method outlined below.

The children could put a small square of blotting paper over a plastic cup three-quarters full of water. They should cut a strip down to the centre of the paper, and fold the strip back so that it dips into the water. Tell them to mark a spot of coloured ink on to the centre of the paper at the end of the strip and watch what happens. Can they see more than one colour once the water has risen up the strip of paper to the coloured spot? What happens if they repeat this activity using a different coloured felt pen?

The children could make poster displays to share the outcome of the activities with the rest of the class.

Investigative skills
The children have carried out investigations, made observations and explained what happened through their posters.

Content
Many processed foods and drinks contain colourings which have been added to make them look more attractive and to make them tastier. Some of these may cause allergies or may cause children to become hyperactive.

The process of separating the coloured dyes present in Smarties or in the ink from the pens is known as chromatography. When the ink is spotted on to the blotting paper or filter paper and the spot enlarged by slowly dropping water on to the centre of the spot, the different components of the dye in the ink spread out at different rates. Colours are often made up of more than one dye and chromatography can be used to separate the individual colours.

Water is the solvent in this case, and in the activity involving the felt pens, the water rises up the strip of blotting paper by capillarity. When it reaches the coloured spot a separation of the different dyes in the ink occurs.

In chromatography the separation of the components of the dye depends on their solubility in the solvent (in this case, water) and their attraction to the paper (blotting paper/filter paper).

Safety
Do not let the children eat the Smarties – the colouring on them may cause allergies/ hyperactivity in some children.

AT1/3d; AT3/5a PoS

6. Bubbling

Age range
Key Stage 2.

Group size
Small groups.

What you need
A recipe for a sponge cake, ingredients for cake mix; baking powder, bicarbonate of soda, vinegar, water; teaspoons, yoghurt pots, jars, beakers.

What to do
This activity can be introduced with a discussion 'What makes cakes rise? Where do the 'holes' in sponge cakes come from?'

The children can carry out an investigation with bicarbonate of soda and vinegar. What happens when the two are mixed? What do the children observe? Do they hear fizzing or see bubbles in the liquid? Explain to the children that the acid (the vinegar) is reacting with the bicarbonate of soda and carbon dioxide gas is being given off. Tell the children that baking powder contains the bicarbonate and an acid.

They could repeat the activity using baking powder instead of bicarbonate of soda. Why do we use baking powder in cake making? Show the children the sponge cake recipe and ask them what they think would be the effect of leaving out baking powder from the recipe. They could design an experiment to investigate varying the amount of baking powder in the cakes. Encourage questions such as 'What happens if double the amount of baking powder is used?'

The children should make close observations of the cakes when they are made. The children can record their results by making posters describing their investigations. They should discuss the results of their tests and observations either in groups or as part of a whole class discussion.

Investigative skills
The children have asked questions, suggested ideas and made predictions based on some relevant prior knowledge (acid and bicarbonate react chemically to produce carbon dioxide). They have carried out an investigation using varying amounts of baking powder to make cakes, and explained their results.

Content
A chemical change takes place when the acid (vinegar) reacts with the sodium bicarbonate. Carbon dioxide gas is given off. Cakes are made to rise by using a raising agent such as baking powder. Carbon

dioxide gas is given off from the raising agent (which contains sodium bicarbonate and an acid). It is this gas resulting from the chemical reaction which makes the air bubbles in the sponge cakes. These cakes are lighter as a result.

Safety
Hygiene is very important. Care should be taken when preparing and cooking food. Surfaces should be clean and children should wash their hands thoroughly before cooking.

AT1/4a,4c; AT3/4b PoS(iii)

7. Whole investigation – bread

Age range
Key Stage 1.

Group size
Whole class, pairs or small groups.

What you need
Sliced bread samples of different types – wholemeal bread, white bread, brown bread, wheatgerm bread; a toaster; hand lenses, paper plates.

What to do
How do I introduce the investigation?
The children could be taken to visit a local supermarket to look at the range of breads available. This is a good opportunity to discuss breads from other countries, for example, pitta bread, chapattis, pumpernickel, ryebreads.
What questions might the

children ask?
Discuss the different types of bread which have been brought into the classroom. Encourage the children to ask such questions as 'Why are they different colours?', 'Do the breads feel or taste different?', 'Are there more "holes" in the white bread than the brown?'and 'If the bread is toasted does it look, feel or taste different?' **(AT1/2a)**
What observations might the children make?
The bread can be cut up into squares and close observation of colour, texture and taste can be made for each type of bread. Encourage the children to use their hand lenses to look for similarities and differences in the breads. They should look for any whole pieces of wheat or grains and any fibre particles which may be present. Do the brown breads have a stronger taste? Does the crust have a stronger taste? Do any of the breads have a 'nutty' taste? Which bread type do the children like best? **(AT1/1a,2b)**
Designing the investigation
An investigation can be carried out on the effects of toasting bread. The children can compare untoasted and toasted bread and look for differences in colour, weight, texture, smell and taste. They could weigh the bread before and after toasting. Why is there a difference in weight?
How will the children record their findings?
A simple chart can be made listing the different types of bread. The children could then write beside the name of the bread, what colour it was, how it tasted and felt when it was untoasted and toasted.
Interpreting the results
Encourage the children to

discuss their observations and to talk about similarities and differences between the different breads and the untoasted and toasted breads. If they have weighed the bread before and after toasting, talk about why the toasted bread is lighter in weight. Discuss the amount of water that is put into the dough when bread is being made. **(AT1/2c)**
What else might the children investigate?
The children could examine different types of flour and test the strength of these flours.

Content
Bread can be made from different types of flour. Wholemeal flour includes the whole of the wheat grain. Brown or wheatmeal flours usually contain 80–90% of the wheatgerm. The bran and germ are removed when white flour is milled. Wholemeal or brown flours give variety in colour and flavour to breads. As they contain all, or a high proportion of, the bran and germ in the wheatgrain, breads made with these flours have a limited rise and closer texture than those made with white flours.

Wholemeal bread contains fibre which is good for us because, as we cannot digest it, it helps push the other food through our bodies and removes waste products.

The toasted bread has lost much of its moisture and is therefore lighter in weight and shrunken in size compared to untoasted bread.
(AT3/PoS(i)).

Safety
The children should wash their hands before touching and tasting food. Food should be placed on clean paper plates.

CHAPTER 20

Assessment, record-keeping and evaluation

Assessment involves the teacher in gathering information following a child's interaction with an aspect of scientific activity. The information so obtained is compared with a predetermined standard or level. This standard or level referred to may be loosely defined through experience, for example when work is marked with statements such as 'good' or 'poor', or marks are awarded such as 8/10, or a nod of approval or a frown of disapproval is given. Alternatively, the standard may be more tightly defined by judging children's work against criteria-referenced statements of attainment, as in the National Curriculum. While on the face of it, such a system seems easy to apply, in practice it is much more difficult:

1. The criteria referenced statements need to be fully understood.

2. Decisions need to be made as to what constitutes acceptable achievement. For example, how many parts are required to show attainment on the statement, '... be able to name the main external parts of the human body ...' and what are the main parts, anyway?

3. Even if steps (1) and (2) have been carried out conscientiously, it is often problematic to decide whether work shows positive attainment within published criteria.

Michael Bassey in his Assessment Guide *for* Primary Schools *(1990)* defines the following useful terminology associated with assessment:

Formative assessment *helps inform the teaching process. It is assessment during teaching which enables the teacher to determine what future actions are appropriate in the classroom, for example the work which particular* children should carry out on the evidence of their present performance.

Summative assessment concludes a period of teaching and learning in order to determine what has been learned ...

Informal assessment *arises during the normal day-by-day routine in your classroom; it is based on your informal observation of children at work in the classroom, when they answer questions and discuss investigations, on the items they make and when reading their work. From this wealth of information, judgements and achievements of children against the Statements of attainment may be made. This type of assessment involves the professional judgement of the teacher.*

Formal assessment *arises from specially prepared tasks which provide tangible evidence on which judgements can be made.*

With regard to the National Curriculum it can be seen that while Teacher Assessments (TAs) are informal, producing both formative and summative outcomes, Standard Assessment Tasks (SATs) are formal, giving rise to summative outcomes.

Why assess?

Teachers need to assess for two main reasons.
1. They need to gain information on the progress of individual children so that appropriate activities and experiences may be offered to them in the classroom, to further their learning. This could be obtained through formal assessment but is far more likely to come from informal assessment.
2. They need to provide records of progress for parents which will be based on data collected through assessment. These records will be passed on to other teachers so that they may be able to match more appropriately children's abilities with the schemes of work.

The information for the above will come from the same main source. The number of interactions made with the children each day are enormous, as questions are asked, conversations are overheard, help is requested, work is brought for checking and discussions about a particular investigation or concept take place. Without

being totally aware of it, a teacher carries around in her head a vast amount of information on the abilities and progress of the children and the successes and difficulties they are experiencing with their learning. Other data might come from more formal assessment methods, such as using old Standard Assessment Task questions to check progress or through formal tests.

Assessing in the classroom

A variety of strategies and opportunities are available for the teacher to obtain information on children's achievements and progress with the skills of scientific investigation. It is important that a variety of methods are used because children might indicate their abilities more positively through one approach, for example by talking, than through another, such as writing, while others may prefer and perform better on the personal and 'private' aspect of writing when compared to the 'public' forum

of discussion. Some of the advantages and disadvantages of these methods are discussed below.

Questioning

Open and closed questions may be asked to gain a wealth of information about your children's investigational abilities. The flexible nature of one to one or group questioning enables supplementary questions to be asked to check what was really meant by a child's vaguely worded response or to verify whether omitted detail from a written account was due to forgetfulness or laziness, or due to a lack of understanding and ability. Thus, this type of questioning may play a key role in classroom assessment. This is of course not possible when children carry out formal test items, but is a useful technique to be used in the

current format of the SATs at Key Stage 1. Clearly, open questions will allow for a greater range of responses which may have more assessment potential. However, closed questions will be easier to assess. Examples of open questions would include the following.
• What question would you like to ask about the cars and the slope?
• How did you ensure that you carried out a fair test?
• How do your observations compare with your prediction?
   An example of a closed question would be the following.
• What temperature does your thermometer read?

Discussion

Children may tell us what they have been doing and why they have been doing it in group or class discussions. Ideas, opinions, concerns and conclusions are shared and questions are asked and answered. Children might become involved in discussions, or even arguments, about whether a fair test has been carried out. All these discussions offer you information which may be useful for assessment purposes. It may be difficult initially to assess individual contributions, although this will improve with practice as you gain confidence.

Listening

Opportunities to listen to children's conversations about their work are numerous. To some extent this involves the teacher in a passive role avoiding the temptation to interject with questions or statements such as 'Do you agree with that, Khal?' or 'Abigail, explain that again

Investigation: Growth of seeds			
AT1/3b: 'Observe closely and quantify by measuring using appropriate instruments'			
Skill	**Saj**	**Jennifer**	**Jan**
Ruler selected to measure seedlings	*	*	*
Ruler positioned at top and bottom of seedlings	*	*	+
More than one seedling measured or seedling of average size selected and justified	*	*	+
Skill achieved?	Yes	Yes	No
* Achieved without help + Achieved with help			

more slowly'. However, you will be actively listening and making judgements on the child's learning, and as a result better able to match work more appropriately. In addition, you may have gained assessment information which can be added to records when time allows.

Structured observation

This allows us to closely observe the ways in which the children are working and thinking. It overlaps with 'listening' and 'discussion' above, but the emphasis is placed on watching for specific pre-chosen investigational achievements, for example, how children ask questions or make predictions, whether they carry out a fair test or how they select instruments and measure quantities. Such observations enable assessment of these investigational skills in a more formal way and, while taking place during normal classroom activities, are nevertheless time-consuming. The number of children who can be observed at any one time is limited to a maximum of three or four, at least initially. Teachers will, however, gain

much useful information on how children, for example, take temperatures or handle experimental variables. Time should be set aside for carrying out structured observation with a check sheet which also has room for unexpected outcomes. Interruptions are bound to occur but observation may be resumed once the necessary assistance has been given. An example of a teacher's Observational Check List is shown above.

   This raises a most important point which has been concerning many teachers. Opportunities for, and evidence of, positive achievement occur in our classrooms on numerous occasions everyday. We must ensure that we 'collect' and record some of these but there is no possible way that we can 'collect' them all. Some remain to be found when we look at children's work, but some, and probably many, will be 'lost'. But we should not worry, they will surface again at a later date in another context because the number of interactions between the teacher and her children in a day are numerous. The frenetic teacher galloping around the classroom sweeping in assessment data will be a liability, not an asset, to teaching and learning in the classroom. However, the teacher who makes a few arbitrary assessments prior to the onset of Standard Assessment Tasks cannot be defended. A compromise is required involving a well planned strategy which ensures that assessments are regularly being made during, and maybe at the end, of a topic/theme of teaching.

Children's (written) work

Children's work offers opportunities to make assessments away from the demands of the children and classroom. However, modifications may need to be made to the way in which it is tackled. While comments such as 'good' and 'neat work', and marks such as 8/10 may still have a place, indication of positive achievements within the National Curriculum

should be made explicitly, particularly if the older children are to be involved more in the teaching/learning/ assessment process, which they surely should and must. Analysis of children's written work should give the teacher valuable information on investigation skills. There will be evidence of whether children have posed a question and made a prediction about their investigation, whether they have carried out a fair test and measured the variables and whether they have interpreted their results and considered the validity of the evidence on which conclusions were drawn, but also evidence of aspects of conceptual understanding. As many children find writing tasks difficult and often leave out detail from their investigation reports, assessment of such a piece of work may not show maximum achievement and further questioning may be needed to clarify certain points. You will need to consider whether, and in what form, it is useful to record children's positive

achievements on their work. If a child has carried out a fair test is it more appropriate to write 'fair test achieved' or 'AT1/4b achieved', or do both have their place?

While much of your children's work will be in written form, for example, what we did and found out/ diagram/graph, and so on, alternatives such as tape recordings, drama, setting up equipment for an investigation or model should also be encouraged.

Written tests

The above examples have indicated how both formative and summative assessments may be made in the classroom. Test-type information while being formal in nature may give both formative and summative outcomes. On the whole, however, written tests have tended to be used for summative purposes, except where remediation programmes have been set up following such 'tests'. Tests are, of course, relatively easy to assess, particularly if the response to each question is limited to one or two words. In this case factual information is most easily tested and is quick to assess. However, some children have difficulty with reading, the language used is always problematic and written tests are hardly appropriate to assess exploration skills, particularly if they are out of context. For example, it is better to offer children the opportunity to measure the volume of water in an actual measuring cylinder than to give them a diagram of such an experimental set-up. Nevertheless the Assessment of Performance Unit (APU) devised a number of tasks to

Where do they live?
We all went into the school grounds. First of all we had to find the kind of

places where you can find minibeasts. Under an old log I found some woodlouses. Then we

test children's abilities in planning and carrying out investigations, and these, the activities in this book, or your own investigational tasks could be used to gain information on children's investigational skills. If they are not carried out as a part of normal classroom teaching, investigations are very time-consuming and out of context, which is probably why AT1 skills have been left for teachers to assess themselves, rather than through standard tests.

While the tradition of formal testing in British primary schools has decreased over the last decade or two and has rarely, if ever, been a part of primary science assessment, the introduction of Standard Assessment Tasks as an important part of the National Curriculum may lead some teachers to consider 'tests' as a method of assessing and monitoring progress. If teachers do decide to introduce their own testing they will need to select or write test items carefully. The limitations of this method, like any other, must be clearly understood.

Criteria and assessment

Teacher Assessment in the context of the National Curriculum is not based on a traditional testing model but is criterion-referenced. Thus, according to SEAC (1990) 'A child is assessed in relation to a criterion given by a statement of attainment, and not in relation to other children.'. That is welcome news of course but requires far closer scrutiny. It presupposes that the statements of attainment are clear, criterion-referenced statements which many of them are not, at least as they are written, without explanation! This may be seen with reference to Attainment target 1 – see the table below.

Many of the statements of attainment are not always clearly criterion-referenced, as are statements such as 'can add up two single digit numbers', or 'can measure with a minus 10°C to 110°C thermometer to 2°C accuracy'. For the time being at least, it is unlikely that significant changes will be made or that clarification of each statement

will be given by the assessment agency. It therefore seems up to teams of teachers in schools and families/pyramids of schools to clarify for themselves what these statements really mean and what is required for assessment. Through reading publications by the agencies involved in the National Curriculum and its assessment, and by sharing and critically analysing assessed pieces of work, a consensus will arise. Whether it is the same view as the school in the next village or in another part of the country remains to be seen. Some standardisation may be obtained through moderation, though hopefully this is not at the expense of the children. How 'national', the assessment of the National Curriculum proves to be, remains to be seen.

Recording

'Recording information about pupils' achievement and progress, although important, is only part of the assessment process and not an end in itself (SEAC 1990).

Level	Statement of Attainment	Comment
2b	Make a series of related observations	How many should be in a series? When are observations related?
4b	Carry out a fair test in which they select and use appropriate instruments to measure quantities such as volume and temperature	Do *all* the variables need to be controlled? What does appropriate mean? Do the children have to measure accurately or are selection and use the important factors? If accurate measurement is important, to what degree of accuracy?
5c	Evaluate the validity of their conclusions by considering different interpretations of their experimental evidence	To what degree of sophistication? How many interpretations – two?

You will need to keep records which include details of the scheme of work and programmes of study covered but which serve the following purposes:
• record attainment target and statements of attainment which each child has attempted;
• record the achievement level (level of attainment) which each child has reached for each attainment target;
• provide some evidence to support the levels of attainment recorded;
• give parents, other teachers and schools access to information about children's academic and other achievements in school.

An effective record system

For a record system to be effective and useful it must successfully fulfil the following criteria.
• It must be simple and manageable to complete so that it does not detract from the teaching and learning taking place in the classroom.
• It includes all the information that is required to (a) further learning opportunities in the classroom and (b) fulfil conditions laid down by school, local or national bodies.
• It will enable children to understand the progress they are making.
• Others who read it will be able to gain from it the information they require.
• It will be filled in on the basis of evidence and not conjecture.

A whole-school recording policy and system is clearly required. Many primary and secondary schools within 'families' or 'pyramids' have produced joint record systems which will make the transfer of children's achievements more efficient and worthwhile. We suggest the following possibilities.
1. A whole class teaching plan and record;
2. Class record sheets;
3. Individual children's records.

1. A whole class teaching plan and record
informs the teacher in detail of the work which will be undertaken on a weekly basis and may be used for monitoring purposes at a later date. For example, the teacher would be able to tell if she had covered a particular part of the programme of study or given children an activity which allowed them to indicate whether they had achieved a particular statement and level of attainment?

An example modified from the SEAC Assessment Pack C is shown in Figure 1 below.

2. Class record sheets
contain all the information for *one level* (see Figure 2 below). While giving information on the progress of individual children and the whole class, this type of record lacks the space to include such details as the context of the activity when positive achievement was obtained, what evidence was obtained for the achievement or possible ways to help children in the future. By 'crossing' the tick, a distinction could be made between experiencing a particular statement of attainment and gaining positive achievement.

3. Individual children's records
which may be of two types.
(a) An *individual record sheet* which covers all the

Figure 1

Class 6M	Week ending 25/6		
Curriculum area	**Details of work to be undertaken**	**Statements of attainment**	**Programmes of study**
Science	• Visit to a windmill • Gears as power sources • Forces and windmills • How can I make the sails go faster?	AT4/4b AT4/3c, 4c AT1	AT4/(ii); p 11b AT4/(iii); p 12

Figure 2

Science Level 2 Attainment Targets and Levels													
	AT1			**AT2**				**AT3**		**AT4**				
Names	a	b	c	a	b	c	d	a	b	a	b	c	d	e
Muntu A.	✗	✗	✓	✗	✓	✗		✓		✓	✗	✓		✗
Tom B.	✗	✗	✗	✗	✗	✗	✗	✗	✗	✗	✗	✗	✗	✓
Emily B.	✗	✗	✗	✗	✗	✗	✗	✗	✗	✗	✗	✗	✗	✓
John C.	✗	✗	✗	✗	✗	✗	✗	✗	✗	✗	✗	✗	✗	✓
Prakash D.	✗	✗	✓	✗	✓		✗	✓	✗	✓		✗		✓
Venita A.	✗	✗	✗	✗	✗	✗	✗	✗	✗	✗	✗	✗	✗	✗

statements of attainment for an individual pupil. Each box may be cross-hatched when experienced and coloured in when achieved. Different colours may be used to indicate each year.

This sheet may be used as a summative record for reporting and a formative record for advising further action for the child though the information on which it is based, for example, context, evidence, and so on is non-

SCIENCE RECORD SHEET

Key Stages 1 and 2

Name..

Reception...........{
Yr.1....................{
Yr.2....................{
Yr.3........................{*Teacher's initials and indicator colour for each year*
Yr.4....................{
Yr.5....................{
Yr.6....................{

Level \ AT		1	2	3	4	
1	a					a
	b	▓		▓		b
	c	▓	▓	▓		c
	d	▓	▓	▓		d
2	a					a
	b					b
	c			▓		c
	d	▓		▓		d
	e	▓	▓	▓		e
3	a					a
	b					b
	c					c
	d		▓	▓		d
	e	▓	▓	▓		e
4	a					a
	b					b
	c					c
	d	▓				d
	e	▓	▓			e
5	a					a
	b					b
	c					c
	d	▓				d
	e	▓	▓	▓		e
	f	▓	▓	▓		f
	g	▓	▓	▓		g

SCIENCE AT1 Scientific Investigation		Name......................................		
Statement of attainment	**Notes: Where/when covered; evidence; method of assessment; other.**	**Date 1**	**Date 2**	**Achieved**
AT1/1a	• Topic on clothes, commented on fabrics • Talked about differences of sugar, flour, etc.	14/9	26/9	26/9
AT1/2a	• Asked why some fabrics are rough • Suggested it was for winter clothes because they are warmer	14/9	15/9	15/9
2b	• Sorted fabrics into groups	14/9		
2c				
AT1/3a				

existent. This type of record, however, has the advantage of using only one piece of paper for each child but lacks detailed information about the nature of the activity and the context of the learning.

(b) An individual, more detailed record sheet which addresses each attainment target separately.

In this record sheet (see the table above), the price of having more space for information about the nature of the achievement and assessment is reflected in the additional number of pieces of paper. This would need to be combined with the class record sheet to analyse and summarise assessment information on the whole class.

Evaluation

Having established what is to be taught and assessed in science, having established criteria for assessment and having assessed children's work and recorded their achievements, it is possible for the teacher to evaluate the children's progress and her own, her science scheme of work and own teaching. Teachers might like to ask themselves the following questions at the end of the topic/term/year.

1. Did I accomplish the work (topics/themes/projects)which I set out to teach?
2. Did some children accomplish less than I expected?
3. Was the work sufficiently matched to the children's abilities?
4. Were the children given the opportunity to investigate and thus to achieve the appropriate statements of attainment in AT1? (Look to see if they were covered on your 'Whole class teaching plans'.)

5. Was there an area that the children did not understand, despite it being covered? How might I introduce and teach this particular subject more effectively next time?
6. Were my records useful in furthering children's learning and informing parents, children and teachers about individual progress?

There is little need to get anxious about assessment and record keeping as the vast majority of teachers are assessing (making judgements about) their children throughout the day. What teachers now need to do is to put it on a more formal basis, as discussed above. With a small amount of practice, teacher assessment and evaluation will become a normal part of teaching and learning activities in the classroom.

CHAPTER 21

Resources

A wide range of resources is needed for children to be able to carry out scientific investigations. Children can be restricted by limited resources when designing and planning investigations. Many of the suitable resources will come from collections of everyday junk materials such as plastic lemonade bottles, yoghurt pots or drink cans. Other investigations, however, will need more specialist equipment such as thermometers, measuring cylinders, newton meters or hand lenses. It is important, therefore, that both types of equipment are available.

Resources can be collected over a period of time and will need to be stored so that they are readily accessible to the children. Clear labelling of the resources is necessary and regular checks will need to be made on items with a shorter life such as batteries and bulbs.

Useful everyday items

• yoghurt pots and other plastic food containers;
• drink cans;
• cereal boxes, shoe boxes, newspapers, magazines, catalogues;
• plastic lemonade bottles, washing-up liquid bottles;
• egg boxes;
• corks, bottle tops;
• cotton reels, marbles;
• jam jars;
• balloons;
• plastic spoons, straws;
• wood off-cuts;
• elastic bands.

Helpful organisations

Listed on these pages are names of some organisations which provide useful materials for scientific work.

The Association for Science Education (ASE)

This is an organisation run by teachers for teachers, which provides a national and regional forum for primary teachers. You can join either as an individual teacher or as a school subscriber, and ASE subscriptions are deductable for tax purposes. ASE members receive Primary Science Review (a bi-monthly magazine) and ASE Primary Science (a broadsheet containing ideas for classroom activities). They also get a 10% discount on many educational books, and the association runs its own specialist bookshop.

The association also organises many regional and national activities, including lectures, courses, workshops and exhibitions.

ASE can be contacted at the following address: Association for Science Education, College Lane, Hatfield, Herts AL10 9AA.

Useful addresses

Suppliers of scientific equipment

These companies will provide catalogues and price lists on request:

Berol/Osmiroid) Ltd
Oldmeadow Road
Kings Lynn
Norfolk PE30 4JR

Commotion
Redburn House
Stockingswater Lane
Enfield EN3 7TD

Phillip Harris Ltd
Lynn Lane
Shenstone
Lichfield
Staffs WS14 0EE

Heron Educational Ltd
Carrwood House
Carrwood Road
Chesterfield S41 9QB

Hope Education Ltd
Orb Mill
Huddersfield Road
Oldham
Lancs OL4 2ST

Nottingham Educational Supplies (NES)
Ludlow Hill Road
West Bridgford
Nottingham
NG2 6HD

Sheffield Purchasing Organisation (SPO)
Sheffield City Council
Staniforth Road
Sheffield S9 3GZ

Technology Teaching Systems Ltd (TTS)
Unit 4
Holmewood Fields Business Park
Holmewood
Chesterfield
S42 5UX

The Environment

Aluminium Can Recycling Association
Suite 308
1 Mex House
52 Blucher Street
Birmingham B1 1QU

Council for Environment Education
School of Education
University of Reading
24 London Road
Reading RG1 5AQ

Friends of the Earth
26-28 Underwood Street
London N1 7JQ

National Agricultural Centre
Stoneleigh Park
Kenilworth
Warwickshire CV8 2LZ

Oxfam
274 Banbury Road
Oxford
OX2 7DZ

Royal Society for the Protection of Birds (RSPB)
The Lodge
Sandy
Bedfordshire SG19 2DL

'Watch'
Royal Society for Nature Conservation
The Green
Witham Park
Lincoln LN5 7JR

The Wildfowl and Wetlands Trust
Slimbridge
Gloucestershire GL2 7BT

World Wild Fund for Nature
Panda House
Weyside Park
Catteshall Lane
Godalming
Surrey GU7 1XR

Water

Water Service Association
1 Queen Anne's Gate
London SW1H 9BT

Severn Trent Water Authority
2297 Coventry Road
Birmingham B26 3PU

Sound

Whispering Gallery
St. Paul's Cathedral
London
EC4M 8AD

British Telecom Museum
35 Speedwell Street
Oxford OX1 1RH

Educational Media International (Videos)
235 Imperial Drive
Raynor's Lane
Harrow
Middlesex HA2 7HE

Ourselves

The British Heart Foundation
14 Fitzhardinge Street
London W1H 4DH

Harbutt's Educational Services
(Equipment)
Freepost
Bretton Way
Bretton
Peterborough PE3 8BR

Pictorial Chart Educational
Trust (Posters)
27 Kirchen Road
London W13 0UD

Weather

Meteorological Office
Education Service
Met Office Headquarters
Room JG6
Johnson House
Bracknell
Berkshire RG12 2SY

(Produces a resources
catalogue, leaflets, posters and
a primary teachers' pack for
weather.)

Pictorial Charts Educational
Trust (Posters)
27 Kirchen Road
London W13 0UD

(Produces 'The weather and
you' poster.)

Weather Poster Pack
Scholastic Publications
Westfield Road
Leamington Spa
Warwickshire CV33 0JH

Forces

BBC Educational Developments
(Videos)
PO Box 50
Wetherby
West Yorkshire LS23 7EZ

Supplies *Teaching Science in
the Primary School* which
comprises two 1-hour videos:
Levers, Still Shapes and
Stability and *Materials and
Floating.*

Knowledge and Understanding
of Sciences: Forces
National Curriculum Council
Albion Wharf
25 Skeldergate
York YO1 2XL

Specialised apparatus

Lung Bag Kit (Chapter 8,
Activity 4) can be obtained
from Phillip Harris.
Newton meter (Chapter 7,
Activity 2) can be obtained
from Osmiroid.

References and publications mentioned in the text

1. Bassey, M. (1990): *Trent Assessment Guide for Primary Schools, National Curriculum Key Stage 1* Local Education Authority Publications, London

2. Department of Education and Science, Assessment of Performance Unit (1988): *Science Report for Teachers: 1 'Science at Age 11'*

3. Department of Education and Science and the Welsh Office (1991): *Science in the National Curriculum,* HMSO, London

4. King, Clive (1986): *Stig of the dump,* Penguin Books Ltd

5. Russell, A., Black, P., Bell, J. and Daniels, S. (1991): *'Observation in School Science', Assessment Matters No. 8,* SEAC

6. School Examinations and Assessment Council (1990): *A Guide to Teacher Assessment, Pack C; A Source Book of Teacher Assessment,* Heinemann Education, London

7. Strang, J., Daniels, S. and Bell, J. (1991): *'Planning and Carrying Out Investigations', Assessment Matters No. 6,* SEAC

8. Taylor, R.M. and Swatton, P. (1991): *'Graph Work in School Science', Assessment Matters No. 1,* SEAC

PHOTOCOPIABLES

The pages in this section can be photocopied and adapted to suit your own needs and those of your class; they do not need to be declared in respect of any photocopying licence. Each photocopiable page relates to a specific activity in the main body of the book and the appropriate activity and page references are given above each photocopiable sheet.

Science Investigation Planning Form

Science Investigation Planning Form	
Stage in planning	
What do I want to find out? (Title of my investigation.)	
What do I think will happen? (My prediction.)	
Why I think this will happen.	
What I need to observe, measure or count (dependent variable).	
Equipment needed and units used.	
What I must change, how many changes and by how much (independent variable).	
What I must keep the same to make it a fair test (control variables).	
How many samples will I take?	
My results.	
My conclusion (did the results suggest that my prediction was correct?).	

Investigating water –
how much do I use in a day?

Name: **Date:**

Use of water	How many times?	Total amount used
Drinks		
Cleaning teeth		
Flushing the toilet		
Washing		
Having a shower/bath		
Washing machine		
Dishwasher		
Cooking		

Average amounts of water used

Drink	1 litre	Having a shower	27 litres
Cleaning teeth	1 litre	Washing machine	118 litres per load
Flushing toilet	9 litres		
Washing	9 litres	Dishwasher	40 litres
Having a bath	90 litres	Cooking	20 litres

Investigating the dangers of electricity

Investigating conducting and insulating

Object	Material it is made from	My prediction – conductor or insulator?	Is a conductor (bulb lit up)	Is an insulator (bulb did not light up)
1				
2				
3				
4				
5				
6				
7				
8				
9				

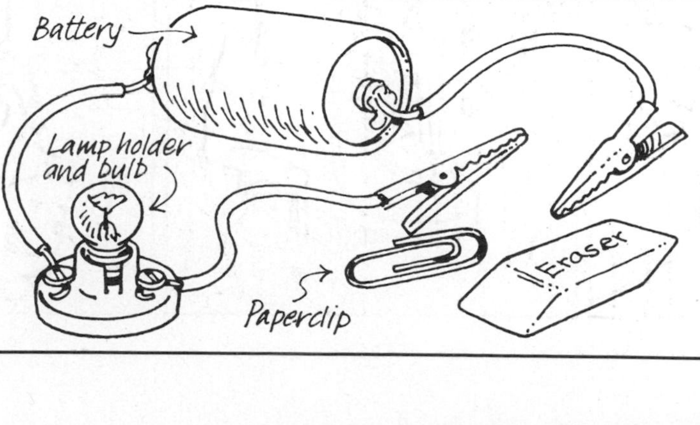

Battery

Lamp holder and bulb

Paperclip

Eraser

Investigating pushes and pulls

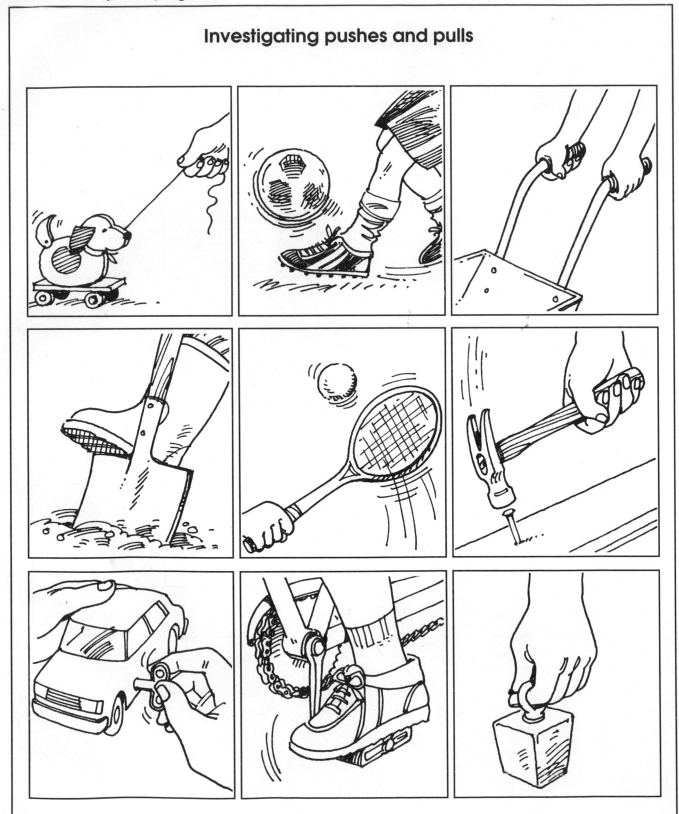

Investigating the pushes and pulls of riding a bicycle

Investigating seasonal changes

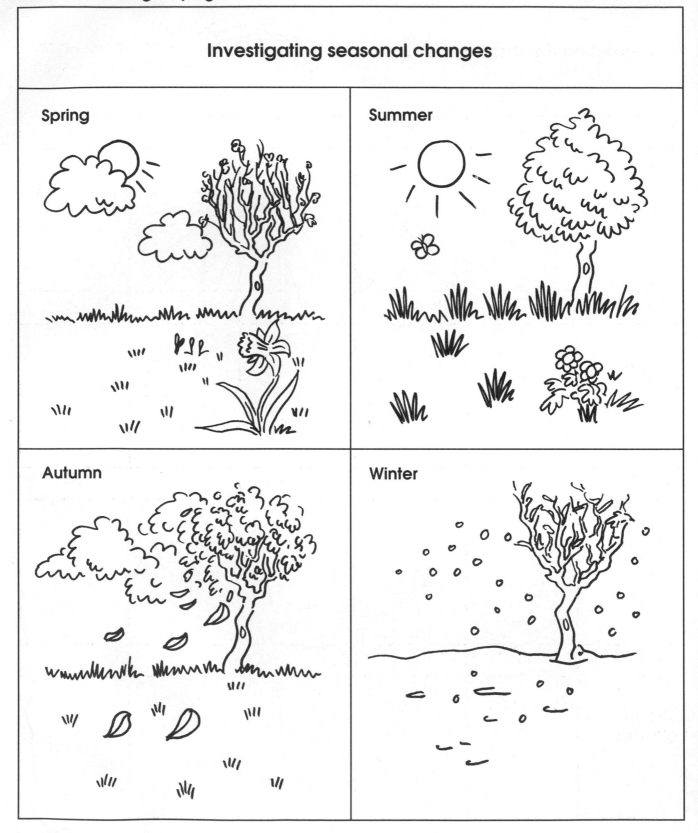

Spring

Summer

Autumn

Winter

Predicting the phases of the moon

○ – New moon which cannot yet be seen

Night	1	4	8	12	15
Shape of moon	○				●

Night	19	23	27	30	34
Shape of moon		◗		○	

Night	38	42	45	49	53
Shape of moon			●		

Night	57	60			
Shape of moon		○			

Investigating the phases of the moon

Night	1	2	3	4	5	6	7
Shape of Moon	◯	◯	◯	◯	◯	◯	◯
Date							
Night	8	9	10	11	12	13	14
Shape of Moon	◯	◯	◯	◯	◯	◯	◯
Date							
Night	15	16	17	18	19	20	21
Shape of Moon	◯	◯	◯	◯	◯	◯	◯
Date							
Night	22	23	24	25	26	27	28
Shape of Moon	◯	◯	◯	◯	◯	◯	◯
Date							
Night	29	30	31	32	33	34	35
Shape of Moon	◯	◯	◯	◯	◯	◯	◯
Date							

Investigating energy – keeping warm at home

Name of family

Type of heating and insulation

1. Central heating						
• gas-fired						
• oil-fired						
• electricity						
• solid fuel						
2. Other forms of heating						
• electric fire						
• gas fire						
• open fire(logs)						
• open fire(coal)						
• open fire (smokeless fuel)						
• paraffin heaters						
• storage heaters						
• other						
3. Insulation						
• hot water tank lagged						
• roof space lagged						
• cavity wall insulation						
• double glazing						
• other						

Investigating fuels and energy

Picture/ Name of item	Will it burn?	Did it burn? If so, how?	Will it make a good fuel?

Investigating minibeasts

Minibeasts found in the school grounds and under logs and stones

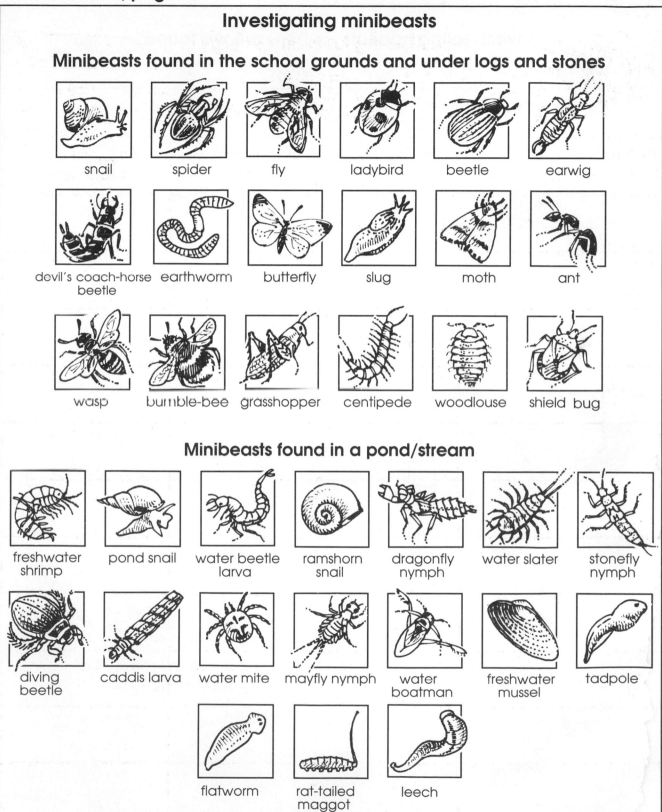

snail

spider

fly

ladybird

beetle

earwig

devil's coach-horse beetle

earthworm

butterfly

slug

moth

ant

wasp

bumble-bee

grasshopper

centipede

woodlouse

shield bug

Minibeasts found in a pond/stream

freshwater shrimp

pond snail

water beetle larva

ramshorn snail

dragonfly nymph

water slater

stonefly nymph

diving beetle

caddis larva

water mite

mayfly nymph

water boatman

freshwater mussel

tadpole

flatworm

rat-tailed maggot

leech

Investigating habitats – where are we found?

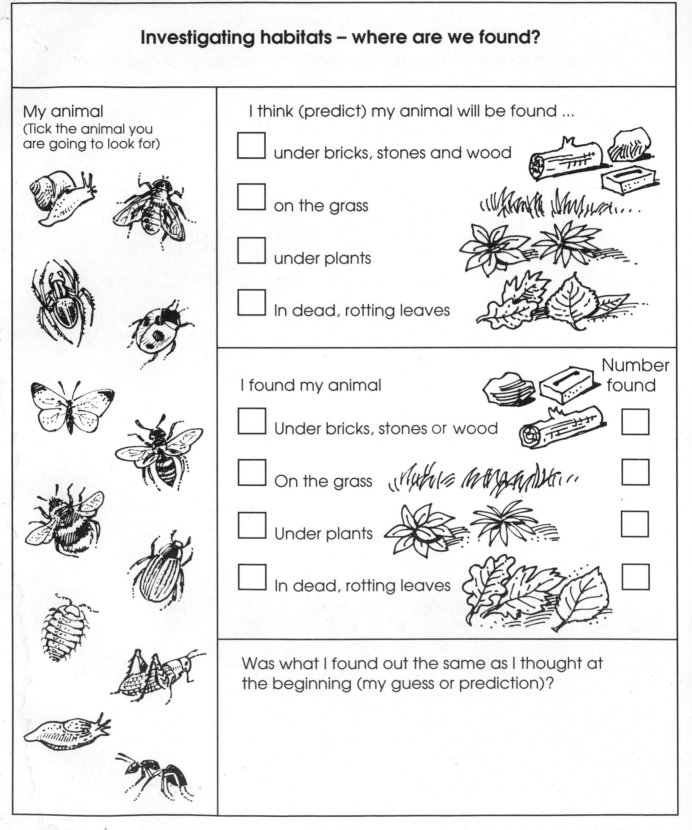

My animal
(Tick the animal you
are going to look for)

I think (predict) my animal will be found ...

☐ under bricks, stones and wood

☐ on the grass

☐ under plants

☐ In dead, rotting leaves

I found my animal

Number
found

☐ Under bricks, stones or wood ☐

☐ On the grass ☐

☐ Under plants ☐

☐ In dead, rotting leaves ☐

Was what I found out the same as I thought at
the beginning (my guess or prediction)?